Course Workbook for the

SAT®

& PSAT®

Version 1.0

Contributors

Very special thanks to the primary instructional authors of this book: Brian Becker, Amy Minster, and Elizabeth Owens.

Special thanks to Deborah A. Silvestrini for her work in producing this edition.

Special thanks also to Aaron Lindh, Bobby Hood, and Erik Kolb for their contributions.

Thank you also to the following individuals who contributed to this edition: Ken Brenner, Joelle Cotham, Jonathan Edwards, Zoe Gannon, Melissa Hendrix, John Moscatiello, Garrison Pierzynski, Rebecca Scott, David Stoll, and Steve Voigt.

—Jonathan Chiu
National Content Director
High School Programs

Contents

SAT: WHAT YOU NEED TO KNOW

INTRODUCTION: THE SAT AND HOW IMPORTANT IS IT, REALLY?

What DOES it all mean, anyway?

S _____

A _____

T _____

How important is it?

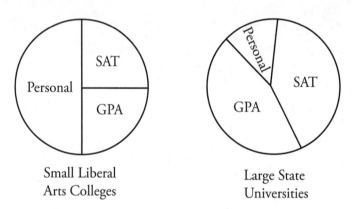

Small Liberal
Arts Colleges

Large State
Universities

What's on the test?

Evidence-based Reading and Writing: _____

Math: _____

"Optional" Essay: _____

The SAT and YOU!

How beatable is the SAT? _____

When is the SAT administered? _____

How many times can you take the SAT? _____

When will YOU take the SAT? _____

Knowing the structure and scoring of the SAT will help you use the techniques and strategies you will learn in this course.

STRUCTURE OF THE SAT

Evidence-based Reading and Writing

	Passages	Questions	Time
Reading			
Writing & Language			

Math

	Multiple-Choice	Grid-In	Extended Thinking	Time
No Calculator				
Calculator				

Essay

Topic: _____ Time: _____

Notes:

- Total time: 3 hours 50 minutes (with Essay).
- Multiple-choice questions have *four answer choices.*
- There is *no penalty* for wrong answers, so don't leave any questions blank.
- Questions are Easy, Medium, or Hard and are each worth 1 point.
- Questions in Math are in a rough order of difficulty.
- Questions in Reading and Writing are NOT in order of difficulty.

How is the SAT scored?

Composite: _____

Two Area scores: _____

Three Test scores: _____

Two Cross-Test scores: _____

Seven subscores: _____

What's a good score?

A good score gets you admitted to the school of your dreams.

A GREAT score gets the admissions people calling you, begging YOU to come to THEIR school!

SAT STRATEGIES

We're going to teach you how to nail every part of the SAT. Each section will have its own approaches and techniques to master. However, there are some strategies that apply across the SAT.

P _____   P _____

O _____   O _____

O _____   E _____

D _____

Pacing

Guessing

L _____

O _____

T _____

D _____

? Why is it better to use LOTD instead of randomizing guesses?

HOW TO USE THIS COURSE TO NAIL THE SAT

Please keep some things in mind as we go through this course:

- This isn't school. We don't give you a grade, but we do expect you to realize that YOUR score improvement reflects the amount of work YOU put into the course.
- The homework assigned is, therefore, for YOUR benefit.
- Try to do at least a half an hour of SAT each day. Like playing an instrument or a sport, preparing for the SAT will be easier (and you will improve faster) if you do at least some work each day. Cramming three hours of SAT practice the night before class won't give you the improvement you can enjoy. Consistent daily practice is the best way to ensure success.
- You *must* try the techniques. Many will seem strange at first. You will get used to them, but only if you practice them.
- Use a pencil! And not only on the bubble sheet: Write all over the test. Seriously. Think on the page, not just in your head.

Setting Goals

Of course, everyone wants to increase his or her score. A big difference between those who succeed and those who don't is whether they set realistic goals and pursue them systematically. Also keep in mind that learning doesn't always happen in a linear fashion or overnight; sometimes it takes a step backwards to take two steps forwards. Don't be discouraged! Keep working in consult with your instructor, and you will enjoy success in the long run.

If you are serious about increasing your scores significantly, then you MUST:

1. Come to ALL the classes.
2. Complete ALL the homework.
3. Come to ALL the diagnostic exams.
4. Use the techniques in class, on the homework, on the diagnostic exams, and on the real SAT.

Your present score:

Math _____ Reading and Writing _____ Essay _____

Your target score:

Math _____ Reading and Writing _____ Essay _____

What are my biggest strengths from the first diagnostic exam?

_____

What are my biggest areas of improvement from the first diagnostic exam?

_____

By the end of this course, I will have accomplished the following (feel free to add more!):

1. _____

2. _____

3. _____

What is the PSAT?

P _____

S _____

A _____

T _____

How Important Is the PSAT?

What Is a National Merit Scholarship?

When Is the PSAT Given?

STRUCTURE OF THE PSAT

Evidence-based Reading and Writing

	Passages	Questions	Time
Reading			
Writing & Language			

Math

	Multiple-Choice	Grid-In	Extended Thinking	Time
No Calculator				
Calculator				

So what's the difference between the PSAT and the SAT?

Reading: _____

_____

Writing & Language: _____

_____

Math: _____

_____

Believe It
The PSAT is now going to be virtually the same in length, structure, and content as the SAT.

READING

WHAT'S COOKING

"A reader lives a thousand lives before he dies...
The man who never reads lives only one."

—George R. R. Martin

Goals Review

At the conclusion of this chapter, you will know:

- The structure of the SAT Reading Test
- Global strategies to earn a higher score

A Variety of Cuisines

The SAT contains one 65-minute Reading Test, composed of 52 multiple-choice questions across five passages, one of which is a dual-passage set. Each passage has 10-11 questions and is 500-750 words in length, and each question has four answer choices. What will the passages be about? Unfortunately, if you're hoping to delve into excerpts from the latest vampire novel or the most recent stats on your favorite football hero, you may be slightly disappointed. Instead, you will see the following:

- One *U.S./World Literature* passage
- Two *History/Social Studies* passages
- Two *Science* passages

Furthermore, some of the passages—specifically one or two of the history or social studies passages, and one of the science passages—will contain charts or graphs.

The Challenges of the Kitchen

Not surprisingly, one of the biggest complaints that students make about the Reading Test is that staying focused on the passages is often difficult. Even if you enjoy reading, perusing a passage on the eating habits of Japanese mice or on the best way to translate the word "taste" from Farsi to English may cause your eyelids to begin to droop. The fact that the 65-minute Reading Test will be the first section of the SAT—when many students are still sleepy-eyed in the early morning—will also be a tremendous challenge. So what can you do?

Keep in mind that your purpose when you read on the SAT is very different from your purpose when you read in school. When you read in school, you're hoping to learn something. You know that you will probably be tested on the information at some later date, and, therefore, you will need to remember something about the book, paper, or journal that you're reading. When you read during the SAT, however, you're not trying to actually discover new information. You're unlikely, for example, to walk out of the SAT thinking, "Wow, I never knew that about phosphorescent fish!" Instead, you're merely reading so that you can answer questions about the passage, and since the SAT is an open-book test, you can always go back to the passage if you missed something. Therefore, rather than reading the whole passage before you start working the questions, go straight to the questions and read only what you need. This way, you're less likely to drift off mid-paragraph.

Planning the Menu

Not all passages are created equal, and based on your POOD, you might opt to do them in a different order than that in which they are presented. Consider the following:

1. **Type of passage**—You may find it easier to focus on a prose fiction passage about a detective than on a science passage about causes of drought near the Colorado River, for example.

2. **Type of question**—Line references that tell you exactly where to find the answer in the passage are often easier than those that simply refer to the passage in general, so a passage that includes many line reference questions may be easier than a passage that does not.

Your goal is to make a quick decision about which of the passages would be the best place for you to start. Find that passage, and do it first. As you move through the Reading Test, save the most challenging passages for last, regardless of where they come in the test.

The SAT gives you all the reading passages at once, so use that to your advantage!

Gathering Your Supplies

Knowing how SAT Reading passages and questions are structured can help you understand how to approach the test as well. The SAT provides you with the following three key items that can help:

• **Line references**: The majority of your SAT Reading questions will refer you to a specific line or set of lines. It's important to note, however, that you'll need to read more than just the lines referenced; to get a solid understanding of the context, read a window of about five lines above and five lines below each line reference.

• **Chronology**: While the first few questions in each passage set may refer to the passage as a whole, the specific questions that follow will appear in loose chronological order through the passage. Therefore, if you find the answer to question 6 in lines 20-25, and the answer to question 8 in lines 38-42, then you should find the answer to question 7 approximately somewhere in the middle, that is, somewhere between lines 25-38. Take advantage of this chronological order to more quickly find the windows to answer questions that don't contain line references.

• **Lead words**: Lead words are words that are easy to find in the passage. These may be words that are italicized, in quotes, or have capital letters. If you're working a question that doesn't have a line reference, look for a lead word that you'll be able to easily spot in the passage.

Selecting the Best Ingredients

With a standardized test, all the right answers are in front of you. The SAT is an open-book test, so ETS will make wrong answers look attractive and right answers seem like they aren't quite what you want. **Your job is to use the text to make a decision about keeping or eliminating answer choices.** Read through each answer and see what you can eliminate because you know for sure it is not supported by the text. If you aren't sure, put an "~" for *maybe* beside the answer. If you like the answer, give it a check mark.

A)	A)	A)	A)
B)	B)	B)	B)
C)	C)	C)	C)
D)	D)	D)	D)

Follow Each Recipe Step

In the Math test, you write out all your steps, don't do work in your head, and track your thinking. You must do the same thing on the Reading test! Mark your windows, underline relevant lines, and physically mark out answers when you're going through POE. If your pencil has stopped moving, you might be stuck. When you get stuck, use your LOTD and move on to the next question.

A TYPICAL STUDENT'S PASSAGE

When you finish a Reading passage, there should be a trail left by your pencil. This trail should track your thinking through the passage, the questions, and the answers. Underlined or bracketed sections, answers crossed out, notes about content or predictions… Let's take a look at what sections of a typical student's passage might look like after they've finished working through it.

Questions 1-11 are based on the following passage.

The following passage discusses the annexation of Hawaii by the United States.

Q1

On January 28, 1893, American read in their evening newspapers a bulletin from Honolulu, Hawaii. Two weeks earlier, said the news report,
Line a group of American residents had overthrown
5 a young native queen and formed a provisional government. Marines from the *U.S.S. Boston* had landed at the request of the American minister in order to protect lives and property. Violence had ended quickly. The rebels were in full control
10 and were said to have enthusiastic support from the populace. Most noteworthy of all, they had announced the intention of asking the United States to annex the islands…

35 Nonetheless, the proposition came unexpectedly, and neither politicians nor journalists knew quite what to make of it. Editorials and comments from Capitol Hill were at first noncommittal. The molders
Q3 of public opinion seemed intent on learning what
40 mold the public wanted…

Q4

Businessmen elsewhere on the Pacific coast
55 followed their lead. San Diego, for example, was virtually the property of the Spreckels family. Moreover, in Los Angeles, Fresno, and San Jose, the Spreckels were allied, to some extent, in the battle against the railroad with merchants,
60 bankers, warehouse owners, real estate dealers, and contractors; and the Chambers of Commerce of
Q6 Portland and Seattle had long cooperated with that of San Francisco in pressing for national policies advantageous to the West. It was not long before
65 businessmen all along the coast were reported as favoring annexation.

1

What event occurred "two weeks earlier" (line 3) than January 28, 1893? *Group overthrew Queen and formed own government*

A) Hawaii became the fiftieth state to join the United States.

B) The United States annexed the Hawaiian islands.

C) American rebels seized governmental control of the Hawaiian islands.

D) Marines from the *U.S.S. Boston* arrived to protect the young native queen from rebels.

3

The tone of the author's statement in lines 37-40 ("Editorials . . . public wanted") is best described as

A) mistrustful.

B) sardonic. *Kind of making fun?*

C) optimistic.

D) pedantic.

4

In describing the response of the "molders" (lines 38-40) the author suggests that they *didn't actually affect opinion*

A) persuaded the United States government to annex the Hawaiian islands.

B) really had little to do with the public's opinion on annexation.

C) were unfamiliar with the politics of the Hawaiian Islands.

D) wanted to learn about the events that took place on the islands.

6

As used in line 63, "pressing" most nearly means

A) requiring urgency. *trying to get*

B) exerting influence.

C) pushing down.

D) extracting information.

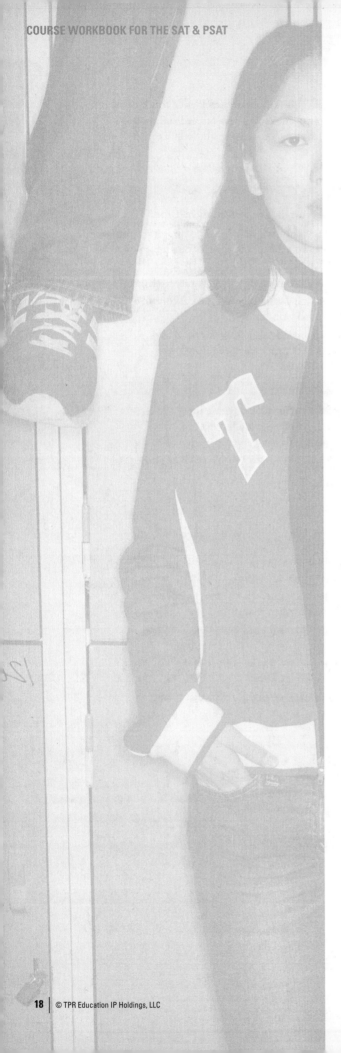

Summary

- The topics of the passages will include:

  _____

  _____

  _____

- What three things can help you find the location of the relevant text for a question?

  1. _____

  2. _____

  3. _____

- Make sure your pencil is

  _____

  _____

- I have accomplished _____ of the _____ goals stated in the Introduction chapter.

BASIC
APPROACH

"If you have enough book space, I don't want to talk to you."

—Terry Pratchett

READING

WRITING AND
LANGUAGE

MATH

ESSAY

Quick Think

Think about the last time you used a cookbook or recipe to make something to eat. Did you read the entire recipe from start to finish, then set the book aside and start cooking, or did you go back and forth as you worked through the instructions? Why are recipes written in steps instead of one big paragraph?

Goals Review

At the conclusion of this chapter, you will have mastered the following:

- Know the five steps of the SAT Reading Basic Approach
- Apply each of the five steps in order to accurately answer questions
- Understand how to use the text to effectively work through answers

SAT READING: BASIC APPROACH

With only 65 minutes to answer 52 questions spread out over five passages, you have to maximize the use of your time. While the inclination might be to thoroughly read the passage and become an expert on the topic, you will end up wasting time on parts of the passage that you don't even need. There are only 10 or 11 questions per passage, so it's a much better use of your time to use the questions to help you focus on the parts of the passage the test writers think are important.

You get points for answering questions, not for reading the passage!

Once you have established the order of your passages, use the following approach for each passage:

1. Read the Blurb
2. Select and Understand a Question
3. Read What You Need
4. Predict the Correct Answer
5. P.O.E.

Step 1: Read the Blurb

That italicized bit at the beginning of each passage may not contain a lot of information, but it will give you a frame of reference for the content of the passage.

Read the following blurb:

> This passage is an excerpt adapted from a book published in 1922 and written by American lawyer and civil libertarian Clarence Darrow. In the passage, Darrow discusses the difficulties involved in defining the words "crime" and "criminal," and the ways in which these words can be interpreted.

Is this passage from *US/World Literature*, *History/Social Studies*, or *Science*? What is the general topic of the passage?

Here is the text of the passage, but we're not going to read it yet. Move on to **Step 2: Select and Understand a Question.**

Don't try to analyze the blurb or read too much into it.

There can be no sane discussion of "crime" and "criminals" without an investigation of the meaning of the words. A large majority of men, even among
Line the educated, speak of a "criminal" as if the word
5 had a clearly defined meaning and as if men were divided by a plain and distinct line into the criminal and the virtuous. As a matter of fact, there is no such division, and from the nature of things, there never can be such a line.

10 Strictly speaking, a crime is an act forbidden by the law of the land, and one which is considered sufficiently serious to warrant providing penalties for its commission. It does not necessarily follow that this act is either good or bad; the punishment
15 follows for the violation of the law and not necessarily for any moral transgression. No doubt most of the things forbidden by the penal code are such as are injurious to the organized society of the time and place, and are usually of such a character
20 as for a long period of time, and in most countries, have been classed as criminal. But even then it does not always follow that the violator of the law is not a person of higher type than the majority who are directly and indirectly responsible for the law.

25 It is apparent that a thing is not necessarily bad because it is forbidden by the law. Legislators are forever repealing and abolishing criminal statutes, and organized society is constantly ignoring laws, until they fall into disuse and die. The laws against
30 witchcraft, the long line of "blue laws," the laws affecting religious beliefs and many social customs, are well-known examples of legal and innocent acts which legislatures and courts have once made criminal. Not only are criminal statutes always dying
35 by repeal or repeated violation, but every time a legislature meets, it changes penalties for existing crimes and makes criminal certain acts that were not forbidden before.

Judging from the kind of men sent to the State
40 legislatures and to Congress, the fact that certain things are forbidden does not mean that these things are necessarily evil; but rather, that politicians believe there is a demand for such legislation from the class of society that is most powerful in political
45 action. No one who examines the question can be satisfied that a thing is intrinsically wrong because it is forbidden by a legislative body.

Other more or less popular opinions of the way to determine right or wrong are found to be no
50 more satisfactory. Many believe that the question of

4

whether an act is right or wrong is to be settled by a religious doctrine; but the difficulties are still greater in this direction. First of all, this involves a thorough and judicial inquiry into the merits of many, if not
55 all, forms of religion, an investigation which has never been made, and from the nature of things cannot be made. The fact is, that one's religious opinions are settled long before he begins to investigate and quite by other processes than reason.
60 Then, too, all religious precepts rest on interpretation, and even the things that seem the plainest have ever been subject to manifold and sometimes conflicting construction. Few if any religious commands can be, or ever were, implicitly relied on without
65 interpretation. The command, "Thou shalt not kill," seems plain, but does even this furnish an infallible rule of conduct?

Of course this commandment could not be meant to forbid killing animals. Yet there are many
70 people who believe that it does, or at least should. No Christian state makes it apply to men killing in war. Neither can it be held to apply to accidental killings, or killings in self-defense, or in defense of property or family. Laws, too, provide all grades of
75 punishment for different kinds of killing, from very light penalties up to death. Manifestly, then, the commandment must be interpreted, "Thou shalt not kill when it is wrong to kill," and therefore it furnishes no guide to conduct. As well say: "Thou shalt do nothing that is wrong."

Step 2: Select and Understand a Question

The first few questions in each question set will often relate to the passage as a whole, while later questions will focus on specific parts of the passage. Start with the specific questions first, and save the general questions for later. The specific questions will be arranged generally in chronological order.

1. The position that Darrow takes is primarily that of

2. In the passage, Darrow draws a distinction between

3. Which choice provides the best evidence for the answer to the previous question?

4. In lines 29-34, Darrow mentions the "laws against witchcraft" and the "blue laws" primarily in order to

5. Lines 39-45 suggest that laws are often created

6. The author's attitude toward the views of the "many" mentioned in lines 50-52 can be described as

7. As used in line 60, "rest" most nearly means

8. Darrow mentions the command "Thou shalt not kill" (line 65) primarily in order to

9. Which choice provides the best evidence for the answer to the previous question?

10. As used in line 66, "furnish" most nearly means

READING

WRITING AND LANGUAGE

MATH

ESSAY

Though Question 1 is the first question in the set, when will you do it? Why?

Once you've chosen a question, take the time to understand what it's asking. SAT Reading questions are often not in question format. Instead, they might make statements such as, "The author's primary reason for mentioning the gadfly is to," and then the answer choices will follow. Make sure that you understand the question by turning it back into a question—that is, back into a sentence that actually ends with a question mark.

4. In lines 29-34, Darrow mentions the "laws against witchcraft" and the "blue laws" primarily in order to

How can you rephrase this into a "what" or "why" question?

Step 3: Read Only What You Need

Many questions will refer you to a specific set of lines or to a particular paragraph, so you won't need to read the entire passage to answer those questions. If you read about five lines above and five lines below each line reference, you should have the necessary information. If you read only the lines from the line reference, you will very likely not find the information you need to answer the question. Read carefully! You should be able to put your finger on the particular phrase, sentence, or set of lines that answers your question. If you save the general questions that relate to the passage as a whole for last, then by the time you begin those questions, you'll have a greater understanding of the passage even if you haven't read it from beginning to end.

Read a window of about 5 lines above and 5 lines below your line reference to get the context for the question.

4. In lines 29-34, Darrow mentions the "laws against witchcraft" and the "blue laws" primarily in order to

Where in the text will you find the answer to this question?

Step 4: Predict the Correct Answer

SAT test writers do their best to distract you by creating tempting but neverthe-less wrong answers. However, if you know what you're looking for before you look at the answer choices, you're less likely to fall for a trap answer. Before you even glance at the answer choices, take the time to think about what specific, stated in-formation in your window supplies the answer to the question. Whenever possible, underline your prediction in the text.

Your prediction should come straight from the text. It is not your opinion or your analysis!

4. In lines 29-34, Darrow mentions the "laws against witchcraft" and the "blue laws" primarily in order to

Based on the text, explain why the author mentions the "laws against witchcraft" and the "blue laws."

Step 5: Use Process of Elimination

Each question has three incorrect answers, and only one correct answer, so it's much easier to find an incorrect answer than it is to find a correct answer. If you can eliminate the wrong answers, then whatever is left must be the correct answer. Physically cross off wrong answers.

Most importantly, eliminate answers that are not consistent with your prediction.

The purpose of predicting is to help you realize that what might otherwise be an appealing answer is wrong because it is not what you are looking for. Avoid the temptation to reconsider your prediction based on an answer choice. The answer choice screaming "pick me!" is likely wrong if it does not match your prediction.

4. In lines 29-34, Darrow mentions the "laws against witchcraft" and the "blue laws" primarily in order to

    A) assert that penalties for certain actions should not be altered. _____ Yes, no, or maybe? Why?
    B) provide illustrations of a previous statement. _____ Yes, no, or maybe? Why?
    C) hint at the value of laws long since repealed. _____ Yes, no, or maybe? Why?
    D) qualify a position by conceding exceptions to a rule. _____ Yes, no, or maybe? Why?

Once you have eliminated all the answers that don't match your prediction, you may still be left with more than one choice. At that point, consider some common wrong answers ETS is likely to give. (We'll look at these in more detail in the next chapter.) Incorrect answers frequently contain the following:

*   Could Be True
*   Mostly Right/Slightly Wrong—it takes only one word or phrase not mentioned in the passage to doom an answer choice
*   Deceptive Language

Use your prediction to eliminate what you can first, and then come back to common traps when you're down to two or three choices.

READING

WRITING AND LANGUAGE

MATH

ESSAY

THE IMPORTANCE OF THE TEXT

Remember, this is not a test in your English class at school. While your English teacher may care about how you use the text to support your opinion, ETS doesn't care about your opinion. The test writers only care that you can read a text and use what's written to support a concrete answer. As you go through POE, you should be asking yourself, "Why?" over and over. "Why keep this? Why get rid of this? Why can I make that choice based on the text? Is that necessarily true?"

Make sure that when you predict the answer, you are using what's actually written, not just what makes sense based on what you read.

5. Lines 39-45 suggest that laws are often created

What is this question asking?

Where in the text will you find the answer?

What *exactly* does the text say about the creation of laws?

Which answer choices can you eliminate?

A)   to prevent wicked actions.
B)   to satisfy the demands of crime victims.
C)   by men who are morally weak.
D)   to appease prevailing political powers.

Another way your comprehension of context will be tested is with **Vocabulary in Context** questions. Although the SAT no longer tests your knowledge of obscure four-syllable words, ETS still cares that you can figure out what words mean. Rather than testing your recall of esoteric definitions, the SAT will now test your ability to figure out secondary meanings of words based on the context in which they are used in the text.

"SAT Words" are a thing of the past! VIC questions will test familiar words in less-familiar contexts.

7. As used in line 60, "rest" most nearly means

When you hear the word "rest," you might think of a soft couch, a fluffy pillow, and a warm blanket. This question is not simply asking you what the word "rest" means, however. It's asking what the word means *in line 60*. You must go back to the text and see how the word is used in context.

Where is the word "rest"?

Mark out the word. Based on the sentence, what other word could you put into the sentence?

Which answer choices can you eliminate, based on your prediction of the correct answer?

A)   recline.
B)   depend.
C)   pause.
D)   conceal.

Paired Questions

Reading the full window carefully is also very important because there will be questions that ask you to cite specific evidence for your answers. These questions will appear in pairs, with the original question first, followed by a question that asks about the specific text to support the answer to the previous question. If you are in the habit of asking yourself, "Why?" during the Predicting and POE steps of the Basic Approach, these questions will simply reinforce what you are already doing.

8. Darrow mentions the command "Thou shalt not kill" (line 65) primarily in order to

What is this question asking?

Where in the text will you find the answer?

What *exactly* does the text say about why Darrow mentions the command?

What answer choices can you eliminate?

A) Argue that even accidental killing or killing in self-defense should be made punishable by law.

B) Demonstrate that even some seemingly straightforward laws may be understood in multiple ways.

C) Provide evidence to show that laws do not punish all types of killings with equal severity.

D) indicate the importance of investigating the religious opinions of those conducting judicial inquiries.

Once you have determined your answer, the next question just asks for the textual evidence you used to reach that answer. Consider what it was in the text that answered your, "Why?" question.

9. Which choice provides the best evidence for the answer to the previous question?

A) Lines 34-38 ("Not only . . . before")

B) Lines 53-59 ("First of all . . . reason")

C) Lines 60-65 ("Then . . . interpretation")

D) Lines 74-76 ("Laws . . . up to death")

General Questions

The general and main idea questions that may seem a bit overwhelming at the beginning of a passage become much more approachable once you've completed the specific questions. You have read and considered the parts of the passage ETS considers to be important. POE will be much more straightforward. Your prediction will be based on your knowledge of the passage as a whole as well as those answers you have already selected.

1. The position that Darrow takes is primarily that of
   A) an authority arguing a particular point of view.
   B) a critic discounting the opinion of an uninformed adversary.
   C) a jurist advocating the right of citizens to defend themselves.
   D) an intellectual presenting a historical overview.

Parallel POE for General Paired Questions

Some of the general questions will be paired questions that have text support from all over the passage or have lead words or ideas that are difficult to find in the passage. These can be very time-consuming, but there are a few strategies you can use to make them much more approachable and efficient. Consider the question and the textual evidence at the same time. Remember, the citation must support the correct answer, so if there are no clear connections between the answer for the question and the line given in the next question, both answers can be eliminated. Consider questions 2 and 3 side-by-side:

2. In the passage, Darrow draws a distinction between	3. Which choice provides the best evidence for the answer to the previous question?
A) actions that are illegal and actions that are morally wrong.	A) Lines 3-7 ("A large . . . virtuous")
B) the opinions of legislators and the rituals of organized society.	B) Lines 26-29 ("Legislators . . . and die")
C) criminals and individuals who are inherently virtuous.	C) Lines 39-42 ("Judging from . . . evil")
D) personal responsibility and responsibility imposed by religious doctrine.	D) Lines 60-63 ("Then, too . . . construction")

Consider the answers in the second column. Do any of the citations in the second column support any of the answers in the first column? If not, eliminate them.

Go back to the text and compare (A) and (C) from the first column based on what Darrow actually says. What distinction is he, the author, making? What's the best answer?

Try these two on your own.

6. The author's attitude toward the views of the "many" mentioned in lines 50-52 can be described as

   A) apathetic.

   B) curious.

   C) puzzled.

   D) skeptical.

10. As used in line 66, "furnish" most nearly means

   A) clothe.

   B) decorate.

   C) provide.

   D) complicate.

READING

WRITING AND LANGUAGE

MATH

ESSAY

DRILL
(11 minutes)

The following passage is excerpted from an auto-biographical novel by Maya Angelou and describes an incident from her youth.

One summer afternoon, sweet-milk fresh in my memory, Mrs. Flowers stopped at the Store to buy provisions. Another Negro woman of her health and
Line age would have been expected to carry the paper
5 sacks home in one hand, but Momma said, "Sister Flowers, I'll send Bailey up to your house with these things."

She smiled that slow dragging smile. "Thank you, Mrs. Henderson. I'd prefer Marguerite, though."
10 They gave each other age-group looks.

Momma said, "Well, that's all right then. Sister, go and change your dress. You going to Sister Flowers's."

There was a little path beside the rocky road, and Mrs. Flowers walked in front swinging her arms and
15 picking her way over the stones.

She said, without turning her head, to me, "I hear you're doing very good school work, Marguerite, but that it's all written. The teachers report that they have trouble getting you to talk in class." We passed
20 the triangular farm on our left and the path widened to allow us to walk together. I hung back in the separate unasked and unanswerable questions.

"Come and walk along with me, Marguerite." I couldn't have refused even if I wanted to. She
25 pronounced my name so nicely. Or more correctly, she spoke each word with such clarity that I was certain a foreigner who didn't understand English could have understood her.

"Now no one is going to make you talk—possibly
30 no one can. But bear in mind, language is man's way of communicating with his fellow man and it is language alone which separates him from the lower animals." That was a totally new idea to me, and I would need time to think about it.

35 "Your grandmother says you read a lot. Every chance you get. That's good, but not good enough. Words mean more than what is set down on paper. It takes the human voice to infuse them with the shades of deeper meaning."

40 She said she was going to give me some books and that I not only must read them, I must read them aloud.

"I'll accept no excuse if you return a book to me that has been badly handled." My imagination
45 boggled at the punishment I would deserve if in fact I did abuse a book of Mrs. Flowers's. Death would be too kind and brief.

The odors in the house surprised me. Somehow I had never connected Mrs. Flowers with food or
50 eating or any other common experience of common people. There must have been an outhouse, too, but my mind never recorded it.

The sweet scent of vanilla had met us as she opened the door.

55 "I made tea cookies this morning. You see, I had planned to invite you for cookies and lemonade so we could have this little chat."

They were flat round wafers, slightly browned on the edges and butter-yellow in the center. With the
60 cold lemonade they were sufficient for childhood's lifelong diet. Remembering my manners, I took nice little lady-like bites off the edges. She said she had made them expressly for me. So I jammed one whole cake in my mouth and the rough crumbs scratched
65 the insides of my jaws, and if I hadn't had to swallow, it would have been a dream come true.

As I ate she began the first of what we later called "my lessons in living." She said that I must always be intolerant of ignorance but understanding of
70 illiteracy. That some people, unable to go to school, were more educated and even more intelligent than college professors. She encouraged me to listen carefully to what country people called mother wit.

When I finished the cookies she brushed off
75 the table and brought a thick, small book from the bookcase. I had read *A Tale of Two Cities* and found it up to my standards as a romantic novel. She opened the first page and I heard poetry for the first time in my life.

80 "It was the best of times and the worst of times . . ."

Her voice slid in and curved down through and over the words. She was nearly singing. I wanted to look at the pages. Were they the same that I had read? Or were there notes, music, lined on the pages, as in a
85 hymn book?

"How do you like that?"

It occurred to me that she expected a response.

The sweet vanilla flavor was still on my tongue and her reading was a wonder in my ears. I had to
90 speak.

I said, "Yes ma'am." It was the least I could do, but it was the most also.

On that first day, I ran down the hill and into the road (few cars ever came along it). I was liked, and
95 what a difference it made. I was respected not as Mrs. Henderson's grandchild or Bailey's sister but for just being Marguerite Johnson.

1

The narrative point of view of the passage is that of

A) a woman explaining the importance of reading.

B) a child presenting her opinions on a particular novel.

C) an adult recounting a memorable childhood experience.

D) a writer describing why she chose to write.

2

In the context of the passage, lines 23-28 ("I couldn't . . . her) are primarily meant to

A) recount an anecdote.

B) describe a theory.

C) present an example.

D) note an impression.

3

As used in line 39, "shades" most nearly means

A) shadows.

B) reflections.

C) levels.

D) insights.

4

In the context of the passage, Marguerite's statement "My imagination boggled at the punishment I would deserve if in fact I did abuse a book of Mrs. Flowers's" (lines 43-47) is primarily meant to convey the idea that

A) Mrs. Flowers is known for her strict and unforgiving nature.

B) Mrs. Flowers is overly concerned with the importance of books.

C) Marguerite would fear for her life if she harmed one of Mrs. Flowers's books.

D) Marguerite is unlikely to mistreat one of Mrs. Flowers's books.

5

According to Mrs. Flowers, which of the following is a "lesson in living"?

A) Intelligence is not dependent on formal education.

B) Intellectuals are not as clever as many people suppose.

C) Well-educated people lack common sense.

D) Impoverished people are deserving of compassion.

6

Which choice provides the best evidence for the answer to the previous question?

A) Lines 40-42 ("She said . . . aloud")

B) Lines 61-62 ("Remembering my . . . edges")

C) Lines 68-70 ("She said . . . illiteracy")

D) Lines 70-72 ("That some . . . professors")

7

Marguerite's statement in lines 76-77 ("I had . . . novel") suggests that she initially viewed *A Tale of Two Cities* as

A) original.

B) sentimental.

C) satisfactory.

D) stunning.

8

In the context of the passage, Marguerite's question in lines 83-85 ("Were they . . . book") primarily serves to

A) imply that Marguerite was bewildered by Mrs. Flowers's unusual speech patterns.

B) show the religious fervor that Mrs. Flowers brought to her reading.

C) indicate that Mrs. Flowers had set the words of the book to music.

D) convey Marguerite's admiration for the eloquence of Mrs. Flowers's reading.

9

Marguerite's attitude toward Mrs. Flowers in lines 87-92 ("It occurred . . . also") is best described as one of

A) respectful awe.

B) grudging acceptance.

C) relaxed affection.

D) guarded fear.

10

Mrs. Flowers's main objective in inviting Marguerite to her house was to

A) help Marguerite to appreciate the importance of the spoken word.

B) urge Marguerite to spend less time reading and more time living.

C) expose Marguerite to a wide variety of literary influences.

D) convince Marguerite to put more effort into her schoolwork.

11

Which choice provides the best evidence for the answer to the previous question?

A) Lines 16-19 ("I hear . . . class")

B) Lines 35-39 ("Your grandmother . . . meaning.")

C) Lines 62-66 ("She said . . . true")

D) Lines 93-95 ("On that . . . made")

Summary

- The five steps of the Reading Basic Approach are:

  1. _____

  2. _____

  3. _____

  4. _____

  5. _____

- How much of the passage do you need to read to find the answer to a specific question?

  _____

  _____

- What's generally true about the order of the questions?

  _____

- How can correct answers on the SAT Reading Test differ from correct answers in an English class?

  _____

  _____

- What is the most important thing to remember in the Reading Test?

  _____

  _____

- I have accomplished _____ of the _____ goals stated in the Introduction chapter.

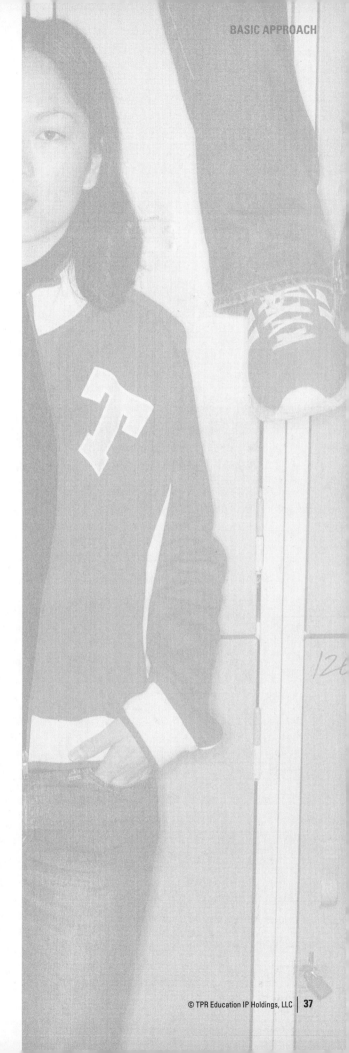

MASTERING POE

"There is more treasure in books than in all the pirate's loot on Treasure Island."

—Walt Disney

Quick Think

Have you ever really, thoroughly cleaned out your closet? Your car? Your room? How do you decide what to keep? What to get rid of? Did you have a process? What was it?

Goals Review

By the end of this chapter, you will be able to:

- Recognize the trap answers ETS gives on Reading questions
- Use Process of Elimination to effectively eliminate wrong answers
- Recognize and identify the major types of Reading questions

MASTER THE POE

Picking up points on the Reading test isn't always about finding the answer that you love the most, but rather about eliminating answers that aren't supported by the text. If you're reading through the answer choices trying to find the best one that answers the question the exact way you would, you might find yourself reading and rereading the answers over and over as your time ticks away.

Instead, retrain yourself to look for the *wrong* answers. By eliminating wrong answers, you leave yourself with the answer that must be right, even if you aren't completely in love with it.

Look for wrong answers instead of right answers.

The best ETS answers:

- Are supported by the text of the passage
- Agree with the main idea of the passage
- Answer the question that's asked

You must read the answer choices carefully. ETS is very good at creating answers that look good with a cursory skim, so make sure you're reading for content. Don't simply match words from the text.

Mark every answer choice as you work through them. Give it a ✓ if you like it, cross it off if you know it's wrong, or give it a ~ if you aren't sure. This gives your brain a visual indicator of where you are in the process of answering the question. If there are no marks, you will continue to reread the answers. Marking them allows you to focus on what's relevant.

A)	A)	A)	A)
B)	B)	B)	B)
C)	C)	C)	C)
D)	D)	D)	D)

It's not uncommon to get down to two answers and then feel stuck. Or feel like you *always* pick the wrong answer. Often, both answers will seem like they could be correct. This is by design. ETS is very good at creating answers that would make sense in an English class when you can explain your opinion. Remember, though, the SAT Reading Test isn't testing your ability to justify your opinion. It's testing your ability to read thoroughly and justify a correct answer using support from the text.

Remember: just because it could be right in an English class doesn't mean it will be right on the SAT!

READING

WRITING AND LANGUAGE

MATH

ESSAY

Down to Two:

Let's take a look at a few pairs of answers. No passages or questions. Which of the following is more likely to be a "best" ETS answer?

A)

B) Suggest that all animal species have consistent migration patterns

C) Provide examples of the various avian migration patterns

D)

A) The college considers the Communication students less valuable than the Pre-med students.

B) More students who complete Pre-med programs go on to further education than students who complete Communication programs.

C)

D)

A)

B) To suggest that current habits are likely to push the blue whale's status to "critically endangered"

C) To argue that the blue whale is destined for extinction

D)

Common Trap Answers

Mostly Right/Slightly Wrong

- ETS is likely to give you a trap answer that mostly looks perfect. Even if 99% of the answer choice is *exactly* what you're looking for, if there's one wrong word, you can eliminate that answer choice. The entire answer must be supported by the text.

Could Be True

- You will find that when you get down to two that both seem logical, if you can put your finger on actual words in the text to support keeping or eliminating an answer, you'll be more accurate. If you're justifying your answer in your head, without using the text, you're likely talking yourself into a trap.

Deceptive Language

- If you aren't reading thoroughly (question, answers, *and* text), and instead are simply matching words, you may find your accuracy negatively affected. ETS will give you answer choices that look really familiar, but don't always say what you want them to say or answer the question that was asked. This could also include answers that are too literal.

Now let's take a look at what to do when you're "Down to Two" on a real passage.

READING

WRITING AND LANGUAGE

MATH

ESSAY

This passage is adapted from Robert M. Yerkes, Ph.D., *The Dancing Mouse: A Study in Animal Behavior.* © 1907 by Macmillan.

The variety of mouse which is known as the Japanese dancing or waltzing mouse has been of special interest to biologists and to lovers of
Line pets because of its curious movements. Haacke,
5 in Brehm's "Life of Animals," writes as follows concerning certain mice which were brought to Europe from China and Japan: "From time to time a Hamburg dealer in animals sends me two breeds of common mice, which he calls Chinese climbing
10 mice and Japanese dancing mice. It is true that the first are distinguished only by their different colors, for their climbing accomplishments are not greater than those of other mice. The color, however, is subject to many variations. Besides individuals of
15 uniform gray, light yellow, and white color, I have had specimens mottled with gray and white, and blue and white. Tricolored mice seem to be very rare. It is a known fact that we also have white, black, and yellow mice and occasionally pied ones,
20 and the Chinese have profited by these variations of the common mouse also, to satisfy their fancy in breeding animals. The Japanese, however, who are no less enthusiastic on this point, know how to transform the common mouse into a really
25 admirable animal. The Japanese dancing mice, which perfectly justify their appellation, also occur in all the described colors. But what distinguishes them most is their innate habit of running around, describing greater or smaller circles or more
30 frequently whirling around on the same spot with incredible rapidity. Sometimes two or, more rarely, three mice join in such a dance, which usually begins at dusk and is at intervals resumed during the night, but it is usually executed by a single
35 individual."

As a rule the dancing mouse is considerably smaller than the common mouse, and observers agree that there are also certain characteristic peculiarities in the shape of the head. One of the
40 earliest accounts of the animal which I have found, that of Landois, states, however, that the peculiarities of external form are not remarkable. Landois further remarks, with reason, that the name dancing mouse is ill chosen, since the human dance movement is
45 rather a rhythmic hopping motion than regular movement in a circle. As he suggests, they might more appropriately be called "circus course mice".

Since 1903 I have had under observation constantly from two to one hundred dancing mice.
50 The original pair was presented to the Harvard Psychological Laboratory by Doctor A.G. Cleghorn of Cambridge. I have obtained specimens, all strikingly alike in markings, size, and general behavior, from animal dealers in Washington,
55 Philadelphia, and Boston. Almost all of the dancers which I have had, and they now number about four hundred, were white with patches, streaks, or spots of black. The black markings occurred most frequently on the neck, ears, face, thighs, hind legs,
60 about the root of the tail, and occasionally on the tail itself. In only one instance were the ears white, and that in the case of one of the offspring of a male which was distinguished from most of his fellows by the possession of one white ear. I have had a few
65 individuals whose markings were white and gray instead of white and black.

All of my dancers had black eyes and were smaller as well as weaker than the albino mouse and the gray house mouse. The weakness indicated
70 by their inability to hold up their own weight or to cling to an object curiously enough does not manifest itself in their dancing; in this they are indefatigable. Frequently they run in circles or whirl about with astonishing rapidity for several minutes
75 at a time. Zoth, who measured the strength of the dancer in comparison with that of the common mouse, found that it can hold up only about 2.8 times its own weight, whereas the common white mouse can hold up 4.4 times its weight. No other
80 accurate measurements of the strength, endurance, or hardiness of the dancer are available. They are usually supposed to be weak and delicate, but my own observations cause me to regard them as exceptionally strong in certain respects and weak in
85 others.

Number of Twirls per Five-Minute Interval

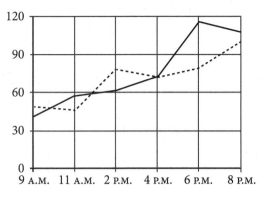

···· Twirls to the Right
— Twirls to the Left

Adapted from data collected by Robert M. Yerkes, Ph.D., and published in *The Dancing Mouse: A Study in Animal Behavior.* © 1907 by Macmillan.

    Yerkes collected data for ten mice at 9 A.M., 11 A.M., 2 P.M., 4 P.M., 6 P.M., and 8 P.M. on a given day. He counted the number of twirls to the left and twirls to the right that the mice made during five
90 minute intervals, and then averaged the number of twirls in each direction. The results are graphed above.

1. The passage suggests that which of the following common assumptions about Japanese dancing mice may be incorrect?

   A)

   B) Dancing mice are generally weak and feeble.

   C)

   D) Dancing mice occasionally perform in small groups, but they more often dance alone.

Deceptive Language

Which answer is the trap answer?

Why?

Which answer is the right answer?

Why?

2. Which choice provides the best evidence for the answer to the previous question?
   A) Lines 31-35 ("Sometimes two . . . individual")
   B)
   C)
   D) Lines 81-85 ("They are . . . others")

Deceptive Language

Which answer is the trap answer?

Why?

Which answer is the right answer?

Why?

9. The author mentions the albino mouse and the gray house mouse (lines 67-69) primarily in order to
   A)
   B) indicate that most types of rodents possess relatively little physical strength.
   C)
   D) contrast the dancing mouse's strength with that of other species of rodents.

Mostly Right/Slightly Wrong

Which answer is the trap answer?

Why?

Which answer is the right answer?

Why?

READING

WRITING AND LANGUAGE

MATH

ESSAY

THIS PAGE IS LEFT INTENTIONALLY BLANK.

READING

WRITING AND LANGUAGE

MATH

ESSAY

The following passage is adapted from a speech given on July 5, 1852, by Frederick Douglass, fugitive slave and Abolitionist.

Pardon me, and allow me to ask, why am I called to speak here today? What have I or those I represent to do with your national independence?
Line Are the great principles of political freedom and
5 natural justice, embodied in that Declaration of Independence, extended to us? And am I, therefore, called upon to bring our humble offering to the national altar, and to confess the benefits, and express devout gratitude for the blessings resulting
10 from your independence to us?

I say it with a sad sense of disparity between us. Your high independence only reveals the immeasurable distance between us. The rich inheritance of justice, liberty, prosperity, and
15 independence bequeathed by your fathers is shared by you, not by me. The sunlight that brought life and healing to you has brought stripes and death to me. This Fourth of July is yours, not mine. You may rejoice, I must mourn. Do you mean, citizens, to
20 mock me, by asking me to speak today?

Fellow citizens, above your national, tumultuous joy, I hear the mournful wail of millions, whose chains, heavy and grievous yesterday, are today rendered more intolerable by the jubilant shouts
25 that reach them. If I do forget, if I do not remember those bleeding children of sorrow this day, "may my right hand forget her cunning, and may my tongue cleave to the roof of my mouth!" To forget them, to pass lightly over their wrongs, and to chime in
30 with the popular theme, would be treason most scandalous and shocking, and would make me a reproach before God and the world.

My subject, then, fellow citizens, is American Slavery. I shall see this day and its popular
35 characteristics from the slave's point of view. In the name of humanity, which is outraged, in the name of liberty, which is fettered, in the name of the Constitution and the Bible, which are disregarded and trampled upon, I will dare to denounce
40 everything that serves to perpetuate slavery.

But I fancy I hear some of my audience say it is just in this circumstance that you and your brother Abolitionists fail to make a favorable impression on the public mind. Would you argue more and
45 denounce less, would you persuade more and rebuke less, your cause would be much more likely to succeed. But, I submit, where all is plain there is

nothing to be argued. What point in the anti-slavery creed would you have me argue? On what branch of
50 the subject do the people of this country need light?

Must I undertake to prove that the slave is a man? That point is conceded already. Nobody doubts it. Would you have me argue that man is entitled to liberty? That he is the rightful owner of
55 his own body? You have already declared it. Must I argue the wrongfulness of slavery? Is that a question for republicans? How should I look today in the presence of Americans to show that men have a natural right to freedom, speaking of it relatively
60 and positively, negatively and affirmatively? To do so makes me ridiculous and would offer an insult your understanding.

Am I to argue that it is wrong to make men brutes, to rob them of their liberty, to work them
65 without wages, to keep them ignorant of their relations to their fellow men, to beat them with sticks, to flay their flesh with the last, to load their limbs with irons, to hunt them with dogs, to sell them at auction, to sunder their families, to knock
70 out their teeth, to burn their flesh, to starve them into obedience and submission to their masters? Must I argue that a system thus marked with blood and stained with pollution is wrong? No; I will not. I have better employment for my time and strength
75 than such arguments would imply.

At a time like this, scorching irony, not convincing argument, is needed. What, to the American slave, is your Fourth of July? I answer: a day that reveals to him more than all other days of
80 the year, the gross injustice and cruelty to which he is the constant victim. To him your celebration is a sham; your denunciation of tyrants, brass-fronted impudence; your shouts of liberty and equality, hollow mockery; your prayers and hymns are to him
85 mere bombast, deception, impiety, and hypocrisy's thin veil to cover up crimes which would disgrace a nation of savages. There is not a nation of the earth guilty of practices more shocking and bloody than are the people of these United States at this very
90 hour.

5. As used in line 57, "republicans" most nearly means

A) a person who is socially conservative.

B) a person living in a democracy.

C)

D)

Could Be True

Which answer is the trap answer?

Why?

Which answer is the right answer?

Why?

6. Douglass asks his audience, "Am I to argue . . . " (lines 63-71) in order to

A) draw attention to the absurdity of the arguments in question.

B) ask his audience for assistance in determining the right subject for the speech.

C)

D)

Too Literal

Which answer is the trap answer?

Why?

Which answer is the right answer?

Why?

8. In lines 81-87, Douglass draws a distinction between

A) the practices of Americans and savages.

B)

C)

D) the ideals and practices of Americans.

Mostly Right/Slightly Wrong

Which answer is the trap answer?

Why?

Which answer is the right answer?

Why?

Remember to focus on what the text actually says.

The passage that follows is adapted from a 1910 short story that follows the actions of Aristide Valentin, head of the Paris police, as he tracks the world's most famous criminal, a clever crook named Flambeau who is a master of disguise.

Flambeau was in England. Probably he would travel as some minor clerk or secretary connected with it; but, of course, Valentin could not be certain.
Line Nobody could be certain about Flambeau.
5   It is many years now since this colossus of crime suddenly ceased keeping the world in a turmoil; and when he ceased, as they said after the death of Roland, there was a great quiet upon the earth. But in his best days (I mean, of course, his
10 worst) Flambeau was a figure as statuesque and international as the Kaiser. Almost every morning the daily paper announced that he had escaped the consequences of one extraordinary crime by committing another. He was a Gascon of gigantic
15 stature and bodily daring; and the wildest tales were told of his outbursts of athletic humour; how he turned the *juge d'instruction* upside down and stood him on his head, "to clear his mind"; how he ran down the rue de Rivoli with a policeman under each
20 arm. Each of his thefts was almost a new sin, and would make a story by itself. It was he who ran the great Tyrolean Dairy Company in London, with no dairies, no cows, no carts, no milk, but with some thousand subscribers. These he served by the simple
25 operation of moving the little milk cans outside people's doors to the doors of his own customers. It was he who had kept up an unaccountable and close correspondence with a young lady whose whole letter-bag was intercepted, by the
30 extraordinary trick of photographing his messages infinitesimally small upon the slides of a microscope. A sweeping simplicity, however, marked many of his experiments. It is said that he once repainted all the numbers in a street in the dead of night merely to
35 divert one traveler into a trap. It is quite certain that he invented a portable mailbox, which he put up at corners in quiet suburbs on the chance of strangers dropping postal orders into it. Lastly, he was known to be a startling acrobat. Despite his huge figure, he
40 could leap like a grasshopper and melt into the tree-tops like a monkey. Hence the great Valentin, when he set out to find Flambeau, was perfectly aware that his adventures would not end when he had found him.

45   But how was he to find him? On this the great Valentin's ideas were still in process of settlement.
There was one thing which Flambeau, with all his dexterity of disguise, could not cover, and that was his singular height. If Valentin's quick eye had
50 caught a tall apple-woman, a tall grenadier, or even a tolerably tall duchess, he might have arrested them on the spot. But all along his train there was nobody that could be a disguised Flambeau, any more than a cat could be a disguised giraffe. About the people
55 on the boat he had already satisfied himself; and the people picked up at Harwich or on the journey limited themselves with certainty to six. There was a short railway official travelling up to the terminus, three fairly short market gardeners picked up two
60 stations afterwards, one very short widow lady going up from a small Essex town, and a very short Roman Catholic priest going up from a small Essex village. When it came to the last case, Valentin gave it up and almost laughed. The little priest was so much the
65 essence of those Eastern flats; he had a face as round and dull as a Norfolk dumpling; he had eyes as empty as the North Sea; he had several brown paper parcels, which he was quite incapable of collecting. The Eucharistic Congress had doubtless sucked out
70 of their local stagnation many such creatures, blind and helpless, like moles disinterred. Valentin was a sceptic in the severe style of France, and could have no love for priests. But he could have pity for them, and this one might have provoked pity in anybody.
75 He had a large, shabby umbrella, which constantly fell on the floor. He did not seem to know which was the right end of his return ticket. He explained with a moon-calf simplicity to everybody in the carriage that he had to be careful, because he had something
80 made of real silver "with blue stones" in one of his brown-paper parcels. His quaint blending of Essex flatness with saintly simplicity continuously amused the Frenchman till the priest arrived (somehow) at Tottenham with all his parcels, and came back for his
85 umbrella. When he did the last, Valentin even had the good nature to warn him not to take care of the silver by telling everybody about it. But to whomever he talked, Valentin kept his eye open for someone else.

READING

WRITING AND LANGUAGE

MATH

ESSAY

1. According to the information in the passage, the Roman Catholic priest can best be described as

   A) burdened and exhausted.

   B) confused and naïve.

   C)

   D)

Could Be True

Which answer is the trap answer?

Why?

Which answer is the right answer?

Why?

2. Which choice provides the best evidence for the answer to the previous question?

   A) Lines 57-64 ("There was . . . laughed")

   B) Lines 71-74 ("Valentin was. . . anybody")

   C) Lines 75-81 ("He had. . . parcels")

   D) Lines 85-89 ("When he. . . else")

Could Be True

Which answer is the trap answer?

Why?

Which answer is the right answer?

Why?

Summary

- What three markings should you use as you work through POE?

  _____

- As you work through the answer choices, you should be looking for _____.

- With Reading, it's important to remember that the correct answers are always

  _____

  _____

  _____.

- What are three common trap answers you'll see on the SAT?

  _____

  _____

  _____

- I have accomplished _____ of the _____ goals stated in the Introduction chapter.

IDENTIFYING THE QUESTION TYPES

"I have always imagined that Paradise will be a kind of library."

— Jorge Luis Borges

READING

WRITING AND LANGUAGE

MATH

ESSAY

Quick Think

You're sitting at a table in the school library. A person sits down next to you. How are your interactions with that person different if she's your best friend rather than the principal of the school? A teacher whose class you love? A teacher whose class you're failing? Why do we act differently around different people?

Goals Review

By the end of this chapter you will be able to

- Identify questions from each category
- Understand specific approaches for each question type

Question Types

All the Reading questions on the SAT fit into one of four categories. Each category requires different tasks, ranging from **retrieving** details explicitly stated in the text to **analyzing** an author's point of view to **synthesizing** information from the text with information in a chart or graph. Recognizing the question types and knowing how to approach each one will help you move through the test more accurately and more efficiently.

Question Categories

- Information and Ideas
- Summarizing
- Rhetoric
- Synthesis

Information and Ideas

The Information and Ideas questions focus on the informational content of the text. Information and Ideas questions will ask you to:

- Identify information and draw reasonable conclusions from the text
- Use given textual support to prove answers

As you work through these questions, make sure you can physically put your pencil on evidence in the text that supports keeping or eliminating certain answers.

Summarizing

The Summarizing questions will ask you to identify a reasonable summary of a section or a summary of the key ideas. These questions will ask you to do two possible things:

- Identify or determine relationships (cause/effect, compare/contrast, sequence…)
- Determine the meaning of words/phrases from context

Use the text to come up with your own answer before you consider the given answers. This will help you match content rather than simply match words.

Rhetoric

The Rhetoric questions focus on analyzing the rhetorical content of the text. This content may include:

- Word choice
- Text structure
- Point of view
- Purpose
- Arguments

With these questions, you are dealing with the purpose of a piece of text, not just what it says. These questions will not just ask *what did the author say?* but instead will ask *why did the author say this?* Of course, the text itself will still supply the answer to the question, but you will search for the author's stated point rather than the details that support the point.

These questions could ask about single words, phrases, larger chunks of text, or the passage as a whole. Read the question carefully to determine whether it would be more efficient to do the question in order with the other questions, or save it until the end of the question sequence.

READING

WRITING AND LANGUAGE

MATH

ESSAY

This passage is adapted from Robert M. Yerkes, Ph.D., *The Dancing Mouse: A Study in Animal Behavior.* © 1907 by Macmillan.

The variety of mouse which is known as the Japanese dancing or waltzing mouse has been of special interest to biologists and to lovers of
Line pets because of its curious movements. Haacke,
5 in Brehm's "Life of Animals," writes as follows concerning certain mice which were brought to Europe from China and Japan: "From time to time a Hamburg dealer in animals sends me two breeds of common mice, which he calls Chinese climbing
10 mice and Japanese dancing mice. It is true that the first are distinguished only by their different colors, for their climbing accomplishments are not greater than those of other mice. The color, however, is subject to many variations. Besides individuals of
15 uniform gray, light yellow, and white color, I have had specimens mottled with gray and white, and blue and white. Tricolored mice seem to be very rare. It is a known fact that we also have white, black, and yellow mice and occasionally pied ones,
20 and the Chinese have profited by these variations of the common mouse also, to satisfy their fancy in breeding animals. The Japanese, however, who are no less enthusiastic on this point, know how to transform the common mouse into a really
25 admirable animal. The Japanese dancing mice, which perfectly justify their appellation, also occur in all the described colors. But what distinguishes them most is their innate habit of running around, describing greater or smaller circles or more
30 frequently whirling around on the same spot with incredible rapidity. Sometimes two or, more rarely, three mice join in such a dance, which usually begins at dusk and is at intervals resumed during the night, but it is usually executed by a single
35 individual."

As a rule the dancing mouse is considerably smaller than the common mouse, and observers agree that there are also certain characteristic peculiarities in the shape of the head. One of the
40 earliest accounts of the animal which I have found, that of Landois, states, however, that the peculiarities of external form are not remarkable. Landois further remarks, with reason, that the name dancing mouse is ill chosen, since the human dance movement is
45 rather a rhythmic hopping motion than regular movement in a circle. As he suggests, they might more appropriately be called "circus course mice".

Since 1903 I have had under observation constantly from two to one hundred dancing mice.
50 The original pair was presented to the Harvard Psychological Laboratory by Doctor A.G. Cleghorn of Cambridge. I have obtained specimens, all strikingly alike in markings, size, and general behavior, from animal dealers in Washington,
55 Philadelphia, and Boston. Almost all of the dancers which I have had, and they now number about four hundred, were white with patches, streaks, or spots of black. The black markings occurred most frequently on the neck, ears, face, thighs, hind legs,
60 about the root of the tail, and occasionally on the tail itself. In only one instance were the ears white, and that in the case of one of the offspring of a male which was distinguished from most of his fellows by the possession of one white ear. I have had a few
65 individuals whose markings were white and gray instead of white and black.

All of my dancers had black eyes and were smaller as well as weaker than the albino mouse and the gray house mouse. The weakness indicated
70 by their inability to hold up their own weight or to cling to an object curiously enough does not manifest itself in their dancing; in this they are indefatigable. Frequently they run in circles or whirl about with astonishing rapidity for several minutes
75 at a time. Zoth, who measured the strength of the dancer in comparison with that of the common mouse, found that it can hold up only about 2.8 times its own weight, whereas the common white mouse can hold up 4.4 times its weight. No other
80 accurate measurements of the strength, endurance, or hardiness of the dancer are available. They are usually supposed to be weak and delicate, but my own observations cause me to regard them as exceptionally strong in certain respects and weak in
85 others.

Q9

Number of Twirls per Five-Minute Interval

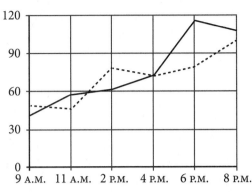

⋯⋯ Twirls to the Right
— Twirls to the Left

Adapted from data collected by Robert M. Yerkes, Ph.D., and published in *The Dancing Mouse: A Study in Animal Behavior.* © 1907 by Macmillan.

Yerkes collected data for ten mice at 9 A.M., 11 A.M., 2 P.M., 4 P.M., 6 P.M., and 8 P.M. on a given day. He counted the number of twirls to the left and
80 twirls to the right that the mice made during five minute intervals, and then averaged the number of twirls in each direction. The results are graphed above.

4. The passage most strongly suggests that Chinese climbing mice are most remarkable for which of the following characteristics?

A) their agility.

B) their lack of strength.

C) their rhythmic movements.

D) their diverse colors.

5. Which choice provides the best evidence for the answer to the previous question?

A) Lines 7-10 ("From time . . . mice")

B) Lines 10-13 ("It is true . . . mice")

C) Lines 27-31 ("But what . . . rapidity")

D) Lines 75-79 ("Zoth . . . its weight")

Information & Ideas—sometimes, the answer is stated almost directly in the text.

Where in the passage will you find this answer?

What does the text actually say?

What is the answer to Question 4?

Even if the answer isn't directly stated, it will still be supported by the text.

READING

WRITING AND LANGUAGE

MATH

ESSAY

6. As used in line 29, "describing" most nearly means

A) explaining.

B) twisting.

C) classifying.

D) outlining.

Information & Ideas

What word of your own could you use instead of "describing"?

See the phrase "in order to"? Remember to answer the *why* question instead of the *what* question!

7. In lines 39-42, the author initially mentions Landois primarily in order to

   A) present an authority who disagreed with the prevailing view.

   B) argue that Japanese dancing mice have no remarkable characteristics.

   C) demonstrate the differences between two different types of rodents.

   D) illustrate the process by which one creature received its name.

Rhetoric

What does the author say about Landois?

Why does the author mention him?

8. According to the information in the passage, the author's attitude toward Landois' claim in lines 43-44 ("the name . . . ill chosen") can best be described as one of

   A) skepticism.

   B) approval.

   C) bewilderment.

   D) indifference.

Rhetoric

Is the attitude positive, neutral, or negative?

What can you eliminate?

What evidence points you to the best answer?

The passage that follows is adapted from a 1910 short story that follows the actions of Aristide Valentin, head of the Paris police, as he tracks the world's most famous criminal, a clever crook named Flambeau who is a master of disguise.

Flambeau was in England. Probably he would travel as some minor clerk or secretary connected with it; but, of course, Valentin could not be certain.

Line Nobody could be certain about Flambeau.

5   It is many years now since this colossus of crime suddenly ceased keeping the world in a turmoil; and when he ceased, as they said after the death of Roland, there was a great quiet upon the earth. But in his best days (I mean, of course, his
10 worst) Flambeau was a figure as statuesque and international as the Kaiser. Almost every morning the daily paper announced that he had escaped the consequences of one extraordinary crime by committing another. He was a Gascon of gigantic
15 stature and bodily daring; and the wildest tales were told of his outbursts of athletic humour; how he turned the *juge d'instruction* upside down and stood him on his head, "to clear his mind"; how he ran down the rue de Rivoli with a policeman under each
20 arm. Each of his thefts was almost a new sin, and would make a story by itself. It was he who ran the great Tyrolean Dairy Company in London, with no dairies, no cows, no carts, no milk, but with some thousand subscribers. These he served by the simple
25 operation of moving the little milk cans outside people's doors to the doors of his own customers. It was he who had kept up an unaccountable and close correspondence with a young lady whose whole letter-bag was intercepted, by the
30 extraordinary trick of photographing his messages infinitesimally small upon the slides of a microscope. A sweeping simplicity, however, marked many of his experiments. It is said that he once repainted all the numbers in a street in the dead of night merely to
35 divert one traveler into a trap. It is quite certain that he invented a portable mailbox, which he put up at corners in quiet suburbs on the chance of strangers dropping postal orders into it. Lastly, he was known to be a startling acrobat. Despite his huge figure, he
40 could leap like a grasshopper and melt into the tree-tops like a monkey. Hence the great Valentin, when he set out to find Flambeau, was perfectly aware that his adventures would not end when he had found him.

45 But how was he to find him? On this the great Valentin's ideas were still in process of settlement.
There was one thing which Flambeau, with all his dexterity of disguise, could not cover, and that was his singular height. If Valentin's quick eye had
50 caught a tall apple-woman, a tall grenadier, or even a tolerably tall duchess, he might have arrested them on the spot. But all along his train there was nobody that could be a disguised Flambeau, any more than a cat could be a disguised giraffe. About the people
55 on the boat he had already satisfied himself; and the people picked up at Harwich or on the journey limited themselves with certainty to six. There was a short railway official travelling up to the terminus, three fairly short market gardeners picked up two
60 stations afterwards, one very short widow lady going up from a small Essex town, and a very short Roman Catholic priest going up from a small Essex village. When it came to the last case, Valentin gave it up and almost laughed. The little priest was so much the
65 essence of those Eastern flats; he had a face as round and dull as a Norfolk dumpling; he had eyes as empty as the North Sea; he had several brown paper parcels, which he was quite incapable of collecting. The Eucharistic Congress had doubtless sucked out
70 of their local stagnation many such creatures, blind and helpless, like moles disinterred. Valentin was a sceptic in the severe style of France, and could have no love for priests. But he could have pity for them, and this one might have provoked pity in anybody.
75 He had a large, shabby umbrella, which constantly fell on the floor. He did not seem to know which was the right end of his return ticket. He explained with a moon-calf simplicity to everybody in the carriage that he had to be careful, because he had something
80 made of real silver "with blue stones" in one of his brown-paper parcels. His quaint blending of Essex flatness with saintly simplicity continuously amused the Frenchman till the priest arrived (somehow) at Tottenham with all his parcels, and came back for his
85 umbrella. When he did the last, Valentin even had the good nature to warn him not to take care of the silver by telling everybody about it. But to whomever he talked, Valentin kept his eye open for someone else.

3. Based on the information in the passage, it can be inferred that Valentin believes that he is most likely to recognize Flambeau through his

   A) athleticism.

   B) stature.

   C) simplicity.

   D) gender.

Information & Ideas

What exactly does the text say about Flambeau's most recognizable feature?

What does this mean?

Which lines did you use to figure this out?

4. Which choice provides the best evidence for the answer to the previous question?

   A) Lines 32-33 ("A sweeping . . . experiments")

   B) Lines 38-39 ("Lastly . . . acrobat")

   C) Lines 47-49 ("There was . . . height")

   D) Lines 52-54 ("But all . . . giraffe")

8. Lines 45-46 provide evidence that Valentin is

   A) determined.

   B) amused.

   C) uncertain.

   D) merciless.

Information & Ideas

What exactly does the text say about Valentin's attitude?

What does this mean?

7. As used in line 40, "melt" most nearly means

   A) thaw.

   B) vanish.

   C) flow.

   D) disintegrate.

Summarizing

What word of your own could you use instead of "melt"?

6. The information in lines 14-41 primarily serves to

   A) illustrate the ingenious and adventuresome nature of a criminal.

   B) outline the type of corruption common in large cities.

   C) reveal the motivations behind one man's mischievous pranks.

   D) evaluate the morality of a crook's actions in light of circumstances.

Rhetoric—Detail

This question has the phrase "serves to." That means you'll be answering the _____ question instead of the _____ question.

What does the author say in those lines?

Why does the author give you that information?

The following passage is adapted from a speech given on July 5, 1852, by Frederick Douglass, fugitive slave and Abolitionist.

Pardon me, and allow me to ask, why am I called to speak here today? What have I or those I represent to do with your national independence?
Line Are the great principles of political freedom and
5 natural justice, embodied in that Declaration of Independence, extended to us? And am I, therefore, called upon to bring our humble offering to the national altar, and to confess the benefits, and express devout gratitude for the blessings resulting
10 from your independence to us?

I say it with a sad sense of disparity between us. Your high independence only reveals the immeasurable distance between us. The rich inheritance of justice, liberty, prosperity, and
15 independence bequeathed by your fathers is shared by you, not by me. The sunlight that brought life and healing to you has brought stripes and death to me. This Fourth of July is yours, not mine. You may rejoice, I must mourn. Do you mean, citizens, to
20 mock me, by asking me to speak today?

Fellow citizens, above your national, tumultuous joy, I hear the mournful wail of millions, whose chains, heavy and grievous yesterday, are today rendered more intolerable by the jubilant shouts
25 that reach them. If I do forget, if I do not remember those bleeding children of sorrow this day, "may my right hand forget her cunning, and may my tongue cleave to the roof of my mouth!" To forget them, to pass lightly over their wrongs, and to chime in
30 with the popular theme, would be treason most scandalous and shocking, and would make me a reproach before God and the world.

My subject, then, fellow citizens, is American Slavery. I shall see this day and its popular
35 characteristics from the slave's point of view. In the name of humanity, which is outraged, in the name of liberty, which is fettered, in the name of the Constitution and the Bible, which are disregarded and trampled upon, I will dare to denounce
40 everything that serves to perpetuate slavery.

But I fancy I hear some of my audience say it is just in this circumstance that you and your brother Abolitionists fail to make a favorable impression on the public mind. Would you argue more and
45 denounce less, would you persuade more and rebuke less, your cause would be much more likely to succeed. But, I submit, where all is plain there is

nothing to be argued. What point in the anti-slavery creed would you have me argue? On what branch of
50 the subject do the people of this country need light?

Must I undertake to prove that the slave is a man? That point is conceded already. Nobody doubts it. Would you have me argue that man is entitled to liberty? That he is the rightful owner of
55 his own body? You have already declared it. Must I argue the wrongfulness of slavery? Is that a question for republicans? How should I look today in the presence of Americans to show that men have a natural right to freedom, speaking of it relatively
60 and positively, negatively and affirmatively? To do so makes me ridiculous and would offer an insult your understanding.

Am I to argue that it is wrong to make men brutes, to rob them of their liberty, to work them
65 without wages, to keep them ignorant of their relations to their fellow men, to beat them with sticks, to flay their flesh with the lash, to load their limbs with irons, to hunt them with dogs, to sell them at auction, to sunder their families, to knock
70 out their teeth, to burn their flesh, to starve them into obedience and submission to their masters? Must I argue that a system thus marked with blood and stained with pollution is wrong? No; I will not. I have better employment for my time and strength
75 than such arguments would imply.

At a time like this, scorching irony, not convincing argument, is needed. What, to the American slave, is your Fourth of July? I answer: a day that reveals to him more than all other days of
80 the year, the gross injustice and cruelty to which he is the constant victim. To him your celebration is a sham; your denunciation of tyrants, brass-fronted impudence; your shouts of liberty and equality, hollow mockery; your prayers and hymns are to him
85 mere bombast, deception, impiety, and hypocrisy's thin veil to cover up crimes which would disgrace a nation of savages. There is not a nation of the earth guilty of practices more shocking and bloody than are the people of these United States at this very
90 hour.

4. As used in line 50, "light" most nearly means
   A) brilliance.
   B) deftness.
   C) enlightenment.
   D) buoyancy.

2. The principal rhetorical effect of the second paragraph is to
   A) suggest that Douglass thinks the audience has played an elaborate trick on him.
   B) explain the difference between being a slave and being a free citizen.
   C) demonstrate how upset Douglass is about the speech he is about to give.
   D) highlight the irony of asking a slave to speak about a holiday whose theme is liberty.

3. The primary purpose of lines 44-47 ("Would you . . . succeed") as they relate to the rest of the passage as a whole is to
   A) discuss criticisms of Abolitionism which Douglass finds legitimate.
   B) explain how the rest of this speech will proceed.
   C) introduce a perspective which Douglass later refutes.
   D) demonstrate how necessary it is for a speaker to flatter an audience.

7. Based on lines 76-90, Douglass's opinion of the Fourth of July celebration at that time was one of
   A) excitement.
   B) disappointment.
   C) liberation.
   D) pride.

11. Douglass's primary rhetorical strategy in this passage is to
   A) persuade his audience by complimenting their morals.
   B) mention a series of arguments and then refuse to make them.
   C) quote legal precedent against the legality of slavery.
   D) offer personal anecdotes as proof of slavery's evils.

Summarizing

What word of your own could you use instead of "light"?

Rhetoric—Passage Based

What does Douglass say in the second paragraph?

What is he trying to do?

Rhetoric—Passage Based

What does Douglass say in the indicated lines?

Does that message agree or disagree with what he says in the rest of the passage?

Rhetoric—Passage Based

Did Douglass feel more positive or more negative about the celebration?

What can you eliminate?

Synthesis

The synthesis questions will ask you to combine information from multiple sources. These questions will appear in two different formats:

- **Paired texts**—one of the passages on the Reading test will be a pair of passages that approach the same topic from different perspectives (general-specific, historical-contemporary, pro-con, etc...)
- **Quantitative information**—in the history and/or science passage(s), you may see tables, charts, or graphs that relate to the passage. You will be asked to analyze the information in the graph, either on its own or in relation to the content of the passage.

Number of Twirls per Five-Minute Interval

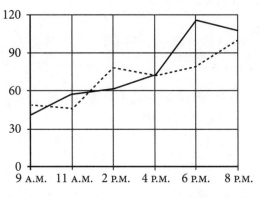

— Twirls to the Left
- - - Twirls to the Right

Adapted from data collected by Robert M. Yerkes, Ph.D., and published in *The Dancing Mouse: A Study in Animal Behavior.* © 1907 by Macmillan.

Yerkes collected data for ten mice at 9 A.M., 11 A.M., 2 P.M., 4 P.M., 6 P.M., and 8 P.M. on a given day. He counted the number of twirls to the left and twirls to the right that the mice made during five minute intervals, and then averaged the number of twirls in each direction. The results are graphed above.

10. Which claim about the dancing mice studied by Yerkes is supported by the graph?

A) During each interval, the dancing mice twirled more often to the right than to the left.

B) At 4 P.M., the mice twirled an equal amount to the right and the left on average.

C) At 9 A.M., the mice twirled more often to the left on average than to the right.

D) As the day progressed, the number of average twirls to the right that the mice made always increased.

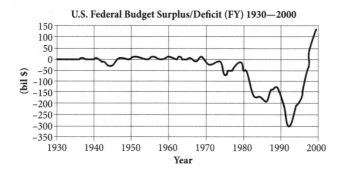

U.S. Federal Budget Surplus/Deficit (FY) 1930—2000

Any number above 0 on the *y*-axis indicates a surplus, while any number below it indicates a deficit.

11. When President Nixon gave his State of the Union address in 1970, he discussed his plan for presenting a balanced budget. Based on the graph, what can you infer about his plan?

A) By cutting more than $7 billion in spending, the Nixon administration was able to produce a surplus for the first time since 1930.

B) Despite the plans he outlined in this speech, Nixon was unable to balance the U.S. budget in 1970.

C) Nixon's spending strategy ensured that the U.S. never again had a budget deficit.

D) Increasing the budget for local law enforcement had long-term negative impacts on the U.S. budget.

Dual Passages

One of the History/Social Studies or Science Reading passages will be dual passages, with two shorter passages about one topic. When you come to do the Dual Passages, focus on each passage individually before you worry about the passages together. Before you **Select a Question**, label all the questions: label with a "1" if the question is about the first passage, a "2" if it's about the second passage, or a "1/2" if it's about both passages.

1. Do all the questions that deal with Passage 1 first.

2. Do all the questions that deal with Passage 2 second.

3. Finally, do the remaining questions that ask about both passages together.

This passage is an excerpt from Charles Darwin's *On the Origin of the Species,* 5th Edition.

Passage 1

As each species tends by its geometrical ratio of reproduction to increase inordinately in number; and as the modified descendants of each species
Line will be enabled to increase by so much the more
5 as they become diversified in habits and structure, so as to be enabled to seize on many and widely different places in the economy of nature, there will be a constant tendency in natural selection to preserve the most divergent offspring of any one
10 species. Hence, during a long-continued course of modification, the slight differences, characteristic of varieties of the same species, tend to be augmented into the greater differences characteristic of the species of the same genus. New and improved
15 varieties will inevitably supplant and exterminate the older, less improved and intermediate varieties; and thus species are rendered to a large extent defined and distinct objects. Dominant species belonging to the larger groups within each class tend to give
20 birth to new and dominant forms; so that each large group tends to become still larger, and at the same time more divergent in character. But as all groups cannot thus succeed in increasing in size, for the world would not hold them, the more dominant
25 groups beat the less dominant. This tendency in the large groups to go on increasing in size and diverging in character, together with the almost inevitable contingency of much extinction, explains the arrangement of all the forms of life, in groups
30 subordinate to groups, all within a few great classes, which has prevailed throughout all time. This grand fact of the grouping of all organic beings under what is called the Natural System, is utterly inexplicable on the theory of creation.
35 As natural selection acts solely by accumulating slight, successive, favourable variations, it can produce no great or sudden modification; it can act only by short and slow steps. Hence the canon of "Natura non facit saltum," which every fresh
40 addition to our knowledge tends to make truer, is on this theory intelligible. We can see why throughout nature the same general end is gained by an almost infinite diversity of means; for every peculiarity when once acquired is long inherited, and structures
45 already diversified in many ways have to be adapted for the same general purpose. We can, in short, see why nature is prodigal in variety, though [stingy] in

innovation. But why this should be a law of nature if each species had been independently created, no
50 man can explain.

This passage is an excerpt from William Paley's *Natural Theology,* 12th Edition.

Passage 2

Were there no example in the world, of contrivance, except that of the eye, it would be alone sufficient to support the conclusion which we draw from it, as to the necessity of an intelligent Creator.
55 It could never be got rid of; because it could not be accounted for by any other supposition, which did not contradict all the principles we possess of knowledge; the principles, according to which, things do, as often as they can be brought to the
60 test of experience, turn out to be true or false. Its coats and humours, constructed, as the lenses of a telescope are constructed, for the refraction of rays of light to a point, which forms the proper action of the organ; the provision in its muscular tendons
65 for turning its pupil to the object, similar to that which is given to the telescope by screws, and upon which power of direction in the eye, the exercise of its office as an optical instrument depends; the further provision for its defence, for its constant
70 lubricity and moisture, which we see in its socket and its lids, in its gland for the secretion of the matter of tears, its outlet or communication with the nose for carrying off the liquid after the eye is washed with it; these provisions compose altogether
75 an apparatus, a system of parts, a preparation of means, so manifest in their design, so exquisite in their contrivance, so successful in their issue, so precious, and so infinitely beneficial in their use, as, in my opinion, to bear down all doubt that can be
80 raised upon the subject. And what I wish, under the title of the present chapter, to observe is, that if other parts of nature were inaccessible to our inquiries, or even if other parts of nature presented nothing to our examination but disorder and confusion, the
85 validity of this example would remain the same. If there were but one watch in the world, it would not be less certain that it had a maker. If we had never in our lives seen any but one single kind of hydraulic machine, yet, if of that one kind we understood
90 the mechanism and use, we should be as perfectly assured that it proceeded from the hand, and thought, and skill of a workman, as if we visited a

museum of the arts, and saw collected there twenty different kinds of machines for drawing water, or
95 a thousand different kinds for other purposes. Of this point, each machine is a proof, independently of all the rest. So it is with the evidences of a Divine agency. The proof is not a conclusion which lies at the end of a chain of reasoning, of which chain
100 each instance of contrivance is only a link, and of which, if one link fail, the whole falls; but it is an argument separately supplied by every separate example. An error in stating an example, affects only that example. The argument is cumulative, in the
105 fullest sense of that term. The eye proves it without the ear; the ear without the eye. The proof in each example is complete; for when the design of the part, and the conduciveness of its structure to that design is shown, the mind may set itself at rest; no future
110 consideration can detract any thing from the force of the example.

1. As used in line 6, "seize" most nearly means
   A) grab hold of.
   B) take advantage of.
   C) shake violently.
   D) blockade.

2. In discussing the number and variety of living species, the author of Passage 1 suggests that
   A) their diversity is totally explained by the theory of creation.
   B) they have been produced through sudden modification.
   C) they are limited by the resources available in nature.
   D) their numbers increase infinitely over time.

3. Which choice provides the best evidence for the answer to the previous question?
   A) Lines 22-25 ("But as . . . dominant")
   B) Lines 31-34 ("This grand . . . creation")
   C) Lines 35-38 ("As natural . . . steps")
   D) Lines 48-50 ("But why . . . explain")

4. As used in line 39, "Natura non facit saltum" refers to
   A) our increasing awareness of natural selection.
   B) sudden modifications in variation.
   C) the infinite diversity of acquired structures.
   D) gradual changes within living species.

5. Based on the information in Passage 1 it can be reasonably inferred that
   A) living species are too similar to be unrelated.
   B) the theory of creation may be able to explain the Natural System.
   C) some improved varieties fail to overtake older varieties.
   D) living species do not demonstrate much variety.

6. Paley's reference to the "coats and humours" in line 61 primarily serves to
   A) inform the reader about the way in which the eye functions.
   B) draw attention to the importance of visual observation.
   C) make an analogy between eyes and telescopes.
   D) demonstrate how the eye does not require the ear.

7. As used in line 84, "confusion" most nearly means
   A) bewilderment.
   B) disorganization.
   C) uncertainty.
   D) ignorance.

8. Paley mentions "the ear" (line 106) primarily in order to
   A) demonstrate how the ear functions independently from the eye.
   B) show how easily his theory might be objected to.
   C) suggest a possible avenue for future research.
   D) illustrate how any single example acts as proof of his argument.

9. The authors of both passages would most likely agree with which of the following?

   A) Individual biological systems are extremely complex and intricately designed.

   B) Dominant groups compete with and displace less dominant groups within the system of nature.

   C) When we observe nature what we see primarily is organization.

   D) All the variety in nature can be explained by sudden and dramatic changes.

10. The passages differ in that Passage 2

    A) considers the hypothesis that species were created by an intelligent designer, while Passage 1 does not.

    B) describes the variation in nature, while Passage 1 focuses primarily on uniformity.

    C) offers a specific example as proof of its claim, while Passage 1 treats the topic in general terms.

    D) is concerned only with the biological development of humans, while Passage 1 is concerned with all species.

11. The tone of both passages is best described as

    A) biased.

    B) certain.

    C) inspired.

    D) belligerent.

READING

WRITING AND LANGUAGE

MATH

ESSAY

THIS PAGE IS LEFT INTENTIONALLY BLANK.

READING

WRITING AND LANGUAGE

MATH

ESSAY

DRILL 1

Time: 12 minutes

This passage is adapted from "Beauty the New Business Tool" by Earnest Elmo Calkins. Copyright Aug 1, 1927, *The Atlantic*.

Some years ago Thomas A. Edison went to Europe. He came to that exquisite gothic jewel, the Chapel of Saint Hubert, which hangs so
Line entrancingly on the castle wall of Amboise, and
5 which everyone knows is the tomb of Leonardo da Vinci. Here Mr. Edison gave out an interview to the gaping newspaper correspondents to the effect that Leonardo was the 'outstanding mechanical genius of his time.' He did not mention that Leonardo was also
10 an artist on the side, either because he did not know or because he did not consider it important. The newspapers commented on the omission, and when an interviewer asked Edison's chum Henry Ford about the comment, Ford remarked that he "would
15 not give five cents for all the art the world had produced." Henry Ford's frank and blunt statement expressed the opinion held by most manufacturers at the beginning of the era of mass production and efficiency, though few were so honest. Those with
20 a weakness for beauty were tempted to conceal it, lest they be suspected of unfitness to have a place in the practical, hard-headed, efficient world. New inventions and discoveries were transforming our industrial system, but when a manufacturer
25 produced a machine that worked he stopped. It never occurred to him to go on and make his device pleasant to look at as well as efficient, managing in those days to reverse William Morris's dictum; they seldom found it necessary to make a thing beautiful
30 in order to make it useful.

It was in those days that Henry Ford began making his famous car. It was an honest piece of work—a motor car that functioned, at an unbelievably low cost— though it did violence to
35 three senses: assaulted sight, jangled hearing, and affronted smell. However, people in those days embraced their wonder at the thing and ignored the intrusion of more ugliness into a world that was losing peace and silence and the beauty that
40 inheres in old things. Mr. Ford rested secure in his belief that he had solved one of the major problems

of human existence and that there was nothing more to be done. About this time Mr. Ford was waited upon by the research expert retained by a
45 publication to study the changing habits of people and their effect on markets for goods. The expert had just completed an exhaustive survey of the trends in the motorcar market and had gone to Detroit to lay his findings before Henry Ford. The
50 survey included two important conclusions: women would be an increasingly important influence in the purchase of cars; beauty in line and color would be the determining factor in selling cars. Mr. Ford's comment was that none of this concerned the Ford
55 Motor Company, and he continued serenely on his way, producing his marvelously efficient car in increasing numbers and selling his product without difficulty.

Meanwhile the making of motor cars passed into
60 its second phase and came under the sway of the cult of beauty. Mechanical improvement had reached its perihelion; the lower-priced cars were becoming dangerously efficient, and it was necessary to do something to justify the price asked for the more
65 costly ones. The big cars were made more sightly. And we had large gorgeously appareled cars at high prices, and small ugly useful cars at low prices. Then Walter Chrysler showed that it was possible to make a small car beautiful, and motor manufacturers
70 realized that people did not demand big cars, but merely cars in which they could take pride. Manufacturers began experimenting with small cars of better appearance. Inspired by this tendency, the Chevrolet Company added design and color to
75 mechanical efficiency, and then for the first time in the history of the motor car the output of the Ford Company was exceeded by a rival manufacturer.

The business of making and selling things must add a new facet to its polyhedron. By the irony of
80 circumstances the type which the manufacturer must now emulate is old Leonardo da Vinci himself, who combined to a rare degree the practical and the imaginative qualities, and whose achievements ranged from the wheelbarrow and the double-spiral
85 staircase at Blois to the *Mona Lisa* and *The Last Supper*.

1

Which of the following best expresses the author's purpose in writing the passage?

A) To criticize an overly broad view

B) To argue the necessity of a shift in perspective

C) To defend a successful position

D) To praise a historic figure

2

Which choice provides the best evidence for the answer to the previous question?

A) Lines 25-30 ("It never occurred . . . useful")

B) Lines 59-61 ("Meanwhile . . . beauty")

C) Lines 73-77 ("Inspired by this . . . manufacturer")

D) Lines 78-79 ("The business of . . . polyhedron")

3

As used in line 8, "outstanding" most nearly means

A) unbelievable.

B) fantastic.

C) distinguished.

D) laudatory.

4

It can be most clearly inferred from the passage that "William Morris's dictum" (lines 26-28)

A) necessitated that a thing be useful in order to be beautiful.

B) suggested that a weakness for beauty need not be concealed.

C) required a creation to often pair functionality with aesthetic appeal.

D) is outdated and unnecessary.

5

The rhetorical impact of listing the words in lines 35-36 ("sight, hearing, and smell") is

A) to evoke in the reader an expectedly familiar association between each word and a regrettable experience.

B) to ineffectively remind the reader of the primary senses which are violently assaulted by dishonest manufacturing practices.

C) to list a variety of ways in which Henry Ford's famous car is unpleasant, despite its economic and functional merits.

D) to overwhelm the reader with the number of ways in which a product of the Ford Motor Company is unappealing.

6

The statement that Ford believed he had "solved one of the major problems of human existence" (lines 41-42) most strongly suggests that Ford

A) believed the quality of his vehicles was unsurpassable.

B) found the dearth of personal motorized travel onerous.

C) had no further work to do once he'd invented his car.

D) had provided a vital necessity.

7

The author uses the word "serenely" (line 55) primarily in order to indicate that

A) Ford found it easy to dismiss expert findings.

B) Ford was scornful of women's growing role in the economy.

C) Ford's success gave him understandable confidence.

D) Ford was strongly entrenched as the peak of his industry.

8

Which choice provides the best evidence for the answer to the previous question?

A) Lines 16-19 ("Henry Ford's . . . honest")

B) Lines 40-43 ("Mr. Ford . . . done")

C) Lines 53-58 ("Mr. Ford's . . . difficulty")

D) Lines 66-67 ("And then we . . . prices")

9

The actions of the Chevrolet Company most clearly indicate an awareness of

A) the research expert's study on trends in the motor car market.

B) the need to surpass the Ford Motor Company in order to dominate the automobile industry.

C) changing values among rising demographics of consumers.

D) mechanical efficiency and beautiful designs and colors.

10

In the context of the passage, "polyhedron" (line 79) most nearly means

A) a solid formed by intersecting planes.

B) market share.

C) a geometric solid.

D) holistic collection of elements.

11

The passage as a whole flows from

A) established philosophy to paradigm shift.

B) personal opinion to corporate consensus.

C) media controversy to artistic license.

D) contested theory to inarguable practice.

READING

WRITING AND LANGUAGE

MATH

ESSAY

THIS PAGE IS LEFT INTENTIONALLY BLANK.

READING

WRITING AND LANGUAGE

MATH

ESSAY

DRILL 2

Time: 12 minutes

This passage is adapted from "The Future of Aerial Transport." Copyright Jan 1928, *The Atlantic*.

The effect of favorable air currents in successful flights, the value of dead reckoning while the wind remains constant in direction, the ceaseless
Line dread that an unknown and therefore incalculable
5 variation of current may occur, the fear of being carried away and lost in the air from drift, the race against time and fuel supply, the discomfort and danger of flying in fog or at freezing heights, the fickleness of wireless, the uncertainty of the 'landfall'
10 in ocean flights, the obstacles to the recognition and choice of landing places—all these and other *navigational* hazards have been demonstrated in turn in all long-distance flights, which are and must remain 'hops for heroes only.' During 1927 the North
15 Atlantic has been crossed four times in nonstop flights; twice only, did the pilots, Charles Lindbergh one of them, arrive and land safely at the intended destination and without mishap, and twelve lives were lost in disastrous ventures, showing only how
20 much weather and wind and sheer luck were the determining factors of triumph or disaster. The efficiency of the machines in the successful flights and the testimony of pilots show the perfection to which the internal-combustion engine has attained,
25 but in the air a trifling mechanical defect may lead to precipitate disaster, for an aeroplane, to keep in the air, must keep going…

The aeroplane had demonstrated its deficiencies and its inherent limitations. Any criticism, however,
30 of the shortcomings of aircraft or any statement of their inherent limitations is met at once by the retort that 'aeroplanes are in their infancy'; that, given time and money for experiment and research, difficulties will be overcome, 'the air will be conquered.'
35 Repeated disappointment and dreadful tragedy are met by the plea that aeroplanes are not yet properly developed, the study of aerodynamics is not sufficiently advanced—and the public is persistently led to expect great improvement in aeroplanes and
40 much practical advance in the art of mechanical flight.

But consideration of the matter will show that flight became possible only after the introduction and development of an engine of light weight per
45 horsepower,—the internal-combustion engine, — and that this engine, continuously improved and developed during the last thirty-five years, has now in all vital respects reached its limit of perfection. All engineering knowledge accumulated since the
50 dawn of the mechanical age has gone generally to the design and construction of the aeroplane as it is to-day; twenty-five years have been devoted to this specialized branch of engineering—mechanical flight. Engineers and experts are agreed on the point
55 that the aeroplane has long passed its experimental stage. The maximum weight that an aero-engine can lift and carry is practically fixed. The engine itself is light; the big factor, apart from the weight of the plane itself, is the fuel it requires. In a long,
60 spectacular flight all the available load must be taken in fuel to cover the distance; no freight can be carried; all but the barest necessities must be left behind. Paying freight can only be taken when the distance is strictly limited: the shorter the distance,
65 the less fuel required, and the more weight left for freight. This at once shows that the aeroplane, for any practical purpose, is a short-distance vehicle of transport.

Leaving profit out of the question, how is
70 commercial success to be achieved for aviation? It is not by further development of the aero-engine, for that has practically, if not quite, reached its limit; not by increasing the size of the planes, for no real saving is thus effected, except in pilots. Engines are
75 as reliable and aeroplanes nearly as perfect as they can well be; external aids are now supplied in plenty, and aerial pilots are expert, ready, and resourceful. Though small improvements will undoubtedly take place, there can be no specific increase in
80 performance. For any spectacular improvement we must await some quite new discovery—some new phenomenon, upon the nature of which it is idle to speculate. It involves a new source of motive energy, any energy which implies little or no weight, but the
85 force of gravity ever pulling the plane and its load to earth, will ever set a limit to the achievements of aircraft and be the insurmountable barrier to commercial success in the air.

Passengers on Imperial Airways Empire Services

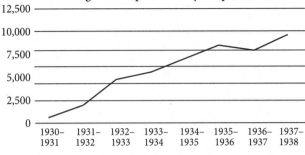

Data obtained from Annual reports of Imperial Airways directors, 1931-1938. "Passenger traffic in the 1930s on British imperial air routes." Pirie, Gordon. http://www.academia.edu/193274/Passenger_traffic_in_the_1930s_on_British_imperial_air_routes_refinement_and_revision

1

The main idea of the passage is that

A) the notion of successful long-distance air travel is overwhelmingly impractical.

B) some minor improvements are necessary before reliable long-distance air travel is plausible.

C) all who believe reliable long-distance air travel will ever be conceivable should be strongly chastised.

D) many regrettable mistakes in the pursuit of reliable long-distance air travel could have been avoided.

2

As used in line 2, "dead" most nearly means

A) deceased.

B) fearful.

C) exact.

D) unavoidable.

3

The primary purpose of the "retort" (line 31) is to

A) demonstrate flawed thinking.

B) engage those with a contrary view.

C) promote common interpretations.

D) alienate critics.

4

As used in line 48, "vital" most nearly means

A) alive.

B) proper.

C) important.

D) known.

5

The main reason given that the aeroplane has long passed its experimental stage is

A) the weight of a plane is practically fixed.

B) the amount of fuel a plane requires is limiting.

C) engine improvements have reached their limit.

D) the number of years devoted to improving planes makes further development impractical.

6

The phrase "for any practical purpose" (lines 66-67) serves primarily to

A) dismiss a commercial suggestion.

B) limit the author's argument.

C) acknowledge important exceptions.

D) provide a technical disclaimer.

7

Which choice provides the best evidence for the answer to the previous question?

A) Lines 1-14 ("The effect of . . . only")

B) Lines 49-54 ("All engineering . . . flight)

C) Lines 57-59 ("The engine . . . requires")

D) Lines 63-66 ("Paying . . . freight.")

8

The phrase "upon the nature of which it is idle to speculate" (lines 82-83) suggests

A) a plea for innovation.

B) a daydream that is best avoided.

C) a pleasant distraction.

D) an imminent discovery.

9

In arriving at a conclusion, the author assumes that

A) the opinions of all experts in the field have been taken into account.

B) gravity prevents researchers from finding a new energy source.

C) no major innovation will dramatically change the nature of flight.

D) there will not be a short series of successful long-distance flights in the next months.

10

It can reasonably be inferred from the passage and graphic that the development of the radio as an airline navigational tool in the early 1930s

A) could not combat travelers' concern about airline safety issues.

B) was a significant factor in advancing the goal of commercial air travel.

C) caused a mid-air collision in 1936.

D) allowed Charles Lindbergh to safely complete his trans-Atlantic flight.

THIS PAGE IS LEFT INTENTIONALLY BLANK.

READING

WRITING AND LANGUAGE

MATH

ESSAY

DRILL 3
Time: 12 minutes

The following passage is adapted from a novel set in the early twentieth century. Lily Bart, a New York socialite, is speaking with her friend Lawrence Selden about some of the differences between the lives led by women and men.

Lily sank with a sigh into one of the shabby leather chairs.

"How delicious to have a place like this all to one's
Line self! What a miserable thing it is to be a woman."
5   She leaned back in a luxury of discontent.

Selden was rummaging in a cupboard for the cake.

"Even women," he said, "have been known to enjoy the privileges of a flat."

10 "Oh, governesses—or widows. But not girls—not poor, miserable, marriageable girls!"

"I even know a girl who lives in a flat."

She sat up in surprise. "You do?"

"I do," he assured her, emerging from the
15 cupboard with the sought-for cake.

"Oh, I know—you mean Gerty Farish." She smiled a little unkindly. "But I said marriageable—and besides, she has a horrid little place, and no maid, and such odd things to eat. Her cook does the
20 washing and the food tastes of soap. I should hate that, you know."

She began to saunter about the room, examining the bookshelves. Suddenly her expression changed from desultory enjoyment to active conjecture, and
25 she turned to Selden with a question. "You collect, don't you—you know about first editions and things?"

He had seated himself on an arm of the chair near which she was standing, and she continued to
30 question him, asking which were the rarest volumes, whether the Jefferson Gryce collection was really considered the finest in the world, and what was the largest price ever fetched by a single volume.

It was so pleasant to sit there looking up at her,
35 as she lifted now one book and then another from the shelves, fluttering the pages between her fingers, while her drooping profile was outlined against the warm background of old bindings, that he talked on without pausing to wonder at her sudden interest in
40 so unsuggestive a subject. But he could never be long

with her without trying to find a reason for what she was doing, and as she replaced his first edition of *La Bruyère* and turned away from the bookcases, he began to ask himself what she had been driving at.
45 Her next question was not of a nature to enlighten him. She paused before him with a smile which seemed at once designed to admit him to her familiarity, and to remind him of the restrictions it imposed.
50 "Don't you ever mind," she asked suddenly, "not being rich enough to buy all the books you want?"

He followed her glance about the room, with its worn furniture and shabby walls.

"Don't I just? Do you take me for a saint on a
55 pillar?"

"And having to work—do you mind that?"

"Oh, the work itself is not so bad—I'm rather fond of the law."

"No; but the being tied down: the routine—don't
60 you ever want to get away, to see new places and people?"

"Horribly—especially when I see all my friends rushing to the steamer."

She drew a sympathetic breath. "But do you
65 mind enough—to marry to get out of it?"

Selden broke into a laugh. "God forbid!" he declared.

She rose with a sigh.

"Ah, there's the difference—a girl must, a man
70 may if he chooses." She surveyed him critically. "Your coat's a little shabby—but who cares? It doesn't keep people from asking you to dine. If I were shabby no one would have me: a woman is asked out as much for her clothes as for herself. The clothes
75 are the background, the frame, if you like: they don't make success, but they are a part of it. Who wants a dingy woman? We are expected to be pretty and well-dressed till we drop—and if we can't keep it up alone, we have to go into partnership."
80 Selden glanced at her with amusement: it was impossible, even with her lovely eyes imploring him, to take a sentimental view of her case.

"Ah, well, there must be plenty of capital on the look-out for such an investment. Perhaps you'll meet
85 your fate tonight at the Trenors."

12

In the context of the passage, Lily's comment in line 10 ("Oh, governesses . . . girls") is primarily meant to

A) express anger about a change in social status.

B) list situations in which women could find themselves.

C) call attention to a person's arrogant behavior.

D) indicate exceptions to a perceived rule.

13

Lily's remarks in lines 16-21 ("Oh . . . you know") help to convey her

A) dislike of a former flatmate.

B) distaste for a certain lifestyle.

C) fear of an uncertain future.

D) contempt for the lower class.

14

The description of Selden's conversation with Lily indicates that Selden is most likely

A) irritated by Lily's childish questions about literature.

B) uncomfortable with her fascination with financial matters.

C) agitated by Lily's casual treatment of his book collection.

D) uncertain about the motivation for Lily's actions.

15

Which choice provides the best evidence for the answer to the previous question?

A) Lines 22-23 ("She . . . bookshelves")

B) Lines 27-33 ("He had . . . volume")

C) Lines 40-44 ("But he . . . at")

D) Lines 52-53 ("He followed . . . walls")

16

As used in line 47, "designed" most nearly means

A) intended.

B) allowed.

C) created.

D) sketched.

17

Selden's response to Lily in lines 54-55 ("Don't I . . . pillar") most directly suggests that he

A) resents not having the time to read any more.

B) wishes to be seen as devoutly religious.

C) agrees that wealth has certain advantages.

D) hopes to move to less shabby apartment soon.

18

Lily's observations in line 71 ("Your coat's . . . cares") serves primarily to

A) ridicule a character.

B) highlight a discrepancy.

C) voice a concern.

D) issue a warning.

19

Lily's remarks about men and women throughout the passage primarily indicate that she views marriage as a

A) natural result of a prolonged courtship.

B) way to learn things that she wouldn't otherwise know.

C) romantic delusion that complicates business.

D) practical necessity for a young woman.

20

Which choice provides the best evidence for the answer to the previous question?

A) Lines 10-11 ("Oh, governesses . . . girls!")

B) Lines 25-27 ("You collect . . . things?")

C) Lines 69-70 ("Ah, there's . . . chooses.")

D) Lines 74-76 ("The clothes . . . it.")

21

In line 85, Selden's use of "fate" refers to the

A) possibility that Lily will meet a potential suitor.

B) likelihood that Lily will be forced to remain single.

C) probability that a business venture will be profitable.

D) belief that Lily faces an unpleasant situation.

Summary

- **Information & Ideas** Questions often ask about the _____ in the passage.

- **Summarizing** questions may ask you to identify relationships such as _____.

  _____

  _____

- **Rhetoric** questions ask about the _____ rather than the _____.

- When faced with Dual Passages, approach the passage as you normally would (preview the questions, work the passage, etc) but go through the passages and questions in a more specific order:

  _____

  _____

  _____

- I have accomplished _____ of the _____ goals stated in the Introduction chapter.

WRITING
AND
LANGUAGE

INTRODUCTION

READING

WRITING AND LANGUAGE

MATH

ESSAY

FUN FACTS ABOUT THE WRITING AND LANGUAGE TEST

The Writing and Language Test gives 35 minutes to answer 44 questions.

- There are four passages with 11 questions each.
- The questions cover a wide range of topics (nearly 40) on both grammar and style.
- There is no order of difficulty in the placement of the passages or of the questions.
- Passages are broken into four topic categories: Careers, History/Social Studies, Humanities, and Science.
- One or more of the passages may feature a figure (chart, graph, etc.).

WRITING AND LANGUAGE: A PROOFREADER AND AN EDITOR

ETS has a number of subcategories and subscores for its test, but those don't mean much. Most of the questions you see on the SAT will fall into one of two categories: Expression of Ideas and Standard English Conventions.

But we call things like we see them. Essentially, on the Writing and Language test, you've got two responsibilities: you need to be a Proofreader and an Editor.

A *proofreader* looks for errors. On the SAT, a proofreader should look for mistakes in grammar, punctuation, and English usage.

An *editor* reviews and improves the writing. On the SAT, an editor should look for ways to improve the continuity and precision of the writing.

THE ANSWERS HOLD THE ANSWER

The vast majority of questions that you see on the SAT will be *proofreader* questions. More often than not, these will be questions with no questions at all, just a sentence with an underlined portion and a list of answer choices.

You've written a **1** book, now it's almost ready for publication.

1. A) NO CHANGE
   B) book, and now
   C) book and now
   D) book, and, now

You may not realize it, but there *is* a question here. Look at the different answer choices. What's similar among them? What's different? The answer to these questions will tell you what the question is testing.

"What's changing in the answer choices?" is the foundational question for all *proofreader* questions. Ask this question every time you're faced with a list of answer choices.

READING

WRITING AND LANGUAGE

MATH

ESSAY

Let's try a few more. There's no passage for these, just the answer choices. What is each one testing?

A) NO CHANGE
B) to run, to jump, and standing still
C) running, having jumped, and standing there still
D) running, jumping, and standing still

What's changing in the answer choices?

_____

What is this question testing?

_____

A) NO CHANGE
B) allusion
C) illusion
D) elision

What's changing in the answer choices?

_____

What is this question testing?

_____

A) NO CHANGE
B) could of
C) could have
D) would of

What's changing in the answer choices?

_____

What is this question testing?

_____

A) NO CHANGE
B) books on a variety of subjects including
C) books, on a variety, of subjects, including
D) books, on a variety of subjects, including

What's changing in the answer choices?

_____

What is this question testing?

_____

A) NO CHANGE
B) valuable and having lots of worth
C) valuable for being worth so much
D) valuable

What's changing in the answer choices?

_____

What is this question testing?

_____

YOUR EARS CAN'T HEAR IT ALL

Your ear is a valuable tool. You don't need to be a grammarian to hear that some things are incorrect. Still, trusting your ear exclusively won't be able to get you all the points that you want.

Make sure to check what's changing in the answer choices. Doing so can reveal mistakes that you might not have otherwise seen or heard.

You wrote the material, but you're not done. Every author still has to make a few more choices about **2** their book.

2. A) NO CHANGE
   B) their books.
   C) his or her book.
   D) your book.

What's changing in the answer choices?

_____

What is this question testing?

_____

One big question is, What will **3** your reader's see first?

3. A) NO CHANGE
   B) you're readers
   C) you're reader's
   D) your readers

What's changing in the answer choices?

_____

What is this question testing?

_____

Written and spoken English are similar, but they're not the same! SAT is testing your knowledge of written English, so make sure that you learn the rules.

POE SAVES THE DAY

Now that you're letting the differences among the answer choices ground your approach to each question, you can work with multiple errors within a single sentence. Determine the substance of each error and use POE to get to the correct answer.

You want to introduce your material **4** somehow. However, that's a complex issue than it may seem.

4. A) NO CHANGE

   B) somehow. However, that's a more complex issue

   C) somehow, however, there's a more complex issue

   D) somehow. However, there's a complex issue

What's changing in the answer choices?

_____

What is this question testing?

_____

You might want to have a Prologue, **5** a Preface, and a Foreword instead.

5. A) NO CHANGE

   B) a Preface, or a Foreword

   C) a Preface or a Foreward

   D) a Preface and a Foreword

What's changing in the answer choices?

_____

What is this question testing?

_____

THE MORE THINGS CHANGE...

Most of us probably use these words [6] interchangeably, but as always, there are differences.

6. A) NO CHANGE
   B) interchangeable, but as always, there
   C) interchangeably. But as always, they're
   D) interchangeably, but as always, they're

What's changing in the answer choices?

_____

What is this question testing?

_____

In most of the Proofreader questions, "NO CHANGE" is the first answer choice. Some people pick it too much. Some don't pick it enough. Avoid either fate by following the approach: *check what's changing in the answer choices, identify the error,* and *use POE.* Many times, the weirdest sentences are the correct ones. Don't fall for the traps!

NO CHANGE is correct about a fourth of the time it appears.
If you've eliminated the other three answer choices, pick
NO CHANGE and move on. Don't force yourself to find
errors where there aren't any!

PACING

Finish the test

Answer all 44 questions, but don't spend time working all of them. If a question seems time-consuming, guess and move on!

Make the obvious POOD choice

On the Writing and Language test, more words usually means more work. The time differential among questions is huge on this test: some questions take 30 seconds while some can take 2 or 3 minutes. The long ones are easy to spot! They usually include long questions followed by wordy answer choices. If you feel pressed for time, skip these questions and move on to the ones you can do more quickly.

Scoring and Pacing

You only have 35 minutes for this section. Get the most points that you can!

Whatever your scoring goals, **finish** the Writing and Language Test.
You may not *work* every question, but you should answer all of them.
Don't get bogged down in wordy questions!
There is probably an easier point later on!

PUNCTUATION

"I'm tired of wasting letters where punctuation will do, period."

—Steve Martin

READING

WRITING AND LANGUAGE

MATH

ESSAY

Goals Review

At the conclusion of this chapter, you will have mastered the following:

- Apply the basic approach to questions dealing with punctuation.
- Know the difference between Stop, Half-Stop, and Go punctuation.
- Know the four situations in which to use a comma.
- Know the two situations in which to use an apostrophe.

STOPS, GOS, PAUSES, AND POSSESSIONS

The list of punctuation errors that SAT will test is actually relatively short. In this chapter, we'll look at punctuation in three main categories. Learn the rules, and these problems will be an absolute snap.

In the meantime, don't forget what we discussed in the Introduction.

Check what changes in the answer choices, and use POE to get to the correct answer.

STOP AND GO

When you are linking ideas,

FANBOYS stands for For, And, Nor, But, Or, Yet, and So.

STOP	HALF-STOP	GO
• Period	• Colon	• Comma
• Semicolon	• Long dash	• No punctuation
• Comma + FANBOYS		
• Question mark		
• Exclamation Mark		

STOP punctuation can link ONLY complete ideas.

HALF-STOP punctuation must be *preceded* by a complete idea.

GO punctuation can link anything EXCEPT two complete ideas.

The rules of punctuation may be a bit of a hassle these **1** days, there are too many marks and rules to learn.

1. A) NO CHANGE
   B) days, there are,
   C) days. There are
   D) days there are

What's changing in the answer choices?

_____

What is this question testing?

_____

Vertical Line Test

Whenever there is Stop or Half-Stop punctuation changing in the answer choices, use the Vertical Line test.

- Draw a vertical line at the proposed punctuation in the question or in the answer choices.
- Determine when you have two complete ideas, a complete and an incomplete idea, or two incomplete ideas.

What comes before, a complete or an incomplete idea?

_____

What comes after, a complete or an incomplete idea?

_____

What CANNOT link these ideas?

_____

There must be a better **2** way, when, we look at the history of punctuation, however, we become newly appreciative of our punctuation marks.

2. A) NO CHANGE
   B) way when we look
   C) way, when we look
   D) way: when we look

What's changing in the answer choices?

_____

What is this question testing?

_____

Does the Vertical Line test apply?

_____

Before the invention of the printing press in **3** the 1400s, books were read only by the educated and wealthy.

3. A) NO CHANGE
   B) the 1400s—books were
   C) the 1400s; books were
   D) the 1400s. Books were

What's changing in the answer choices?

_____

What is this question testing?

_____

Does the Vertical Line test apply?

_____

These volumes had to be transcribed [4] by hand, paper was very expensive.

4. A) NO CHANGE

B) by hand, and paper

C) by hand and paper

D) by hand, and, paper

What's changing in the answer choices?

_____

What is this question testing?

_____

Does the Vertical Line test apply?

_____

Whenever you see FANBOYS underlined,
draw two vertical lines, one on either side.

READING

WRITING AND LANGUAGE

MATH

ESSAY

COMMAS

On the last few pages, you saw two reasons to use a comma: link anything except two complete ideas and FAN-BOYS. SAT will test two other specific uses of the comma, which we will see here.

> Know the four reasons to use a comma.
> If you can't cite one of them, leave the comma out.

After Every Item in a List

As a result, most books prior to the 1400s were written in *scriptura continua*, which had no spaces, no **5** capitalization and no punctuation marks.

5. A) NO CHANGE
   B) capitalization, no punctuation
   C) capitalization, and no punctuation
   D) capitalization, and, no punctuation

What's changing in the answer choices?

_____

What is this question testing?

_____

Before and After Unnecessary Information

This is not to **6** say however, that there was no punctuation before this time.

6. A) NO CHANGE
   B) say however that there was
   C) say, however that there was
   D) say, however, that there was

What's changing in the answer choices?

_____

What is this question testing?

_____

As early as the 5th century BCE, the Greeks were sometimes using punctuation marks, called "dicolons" and "tricolons," to help with the oral transmission of their texts. The [7] number of vertically-arranged dots told speakers the appropriate length of pauses.

7. A) NO CHANGE
   B) number, of vertically-arranged dots, told speakers
   C) number, of vertically-arranged dots told speakers
   D) number of vertically-arranged dots, told speakers

What's changing in the answer choices?

_____

What is this question testing?

_____

Don't Comma Round Here No More

Some other languages, like early Chinese and Mayan, worked in pictograms or [8] syllables rather than individual letters, and thus, had no need for punctuation, at all.

8. A) NO CHANGE
   B) syllables, rather than individual letters and thus, had no need, for punctuation, at all.
   C) syllables rather than, individual letters and, thus, had no need for punctuation, at all.
   D) syllables rather than individual letters and thus had no need for punctuation at all.

What's changing in the answer choices?

_____

What is this question testing?

_____

Which of the four reasons can you cite to use a comma?

_____

There are four reasons to use commas on the SAT:
- Stop punctuation with one of the FANBOYS
- Go punctuation
- After every item in a list
- Before and after unnecessary information

If you can't cite one of these reasons, don't use a comma!

READING

WRITING AND LANGUAGE

MATH

ESSAY

APOSTROPHES

Apostrophes are some of the trickiest punctuation marks in the English language. Look on any billboard, storefront, or (heaven forefend) social media post, and you're likely to find an apostrophe mistake.

Apostrophes are used for possession and contraction. As with commas, if you can't cite a reason to use an apostrophe, don't use one.

With the introduction of the printing press, **9** author's and printer's began to standardize the conventions of written English in they're texts.

9. A) NO CHANGE

   B) authors and printers began to standardize the convention of written English in their texts.

   C) author's and printer's began to standardize the convention of written English in their texts.

   D) authors and printers began to standardize the convention of written English in they're texts.

What's changing in the answer choices?

_____

What is this question testing?

_____

Which of the two reasons can you cite to use an apostrophe?

_____

If you are dealing with nouns (not including pronouns), use an apostrophe to show possession.

Rewrite the following phrases using apostrophes.

i.   The theme of the essay ➔ the _____ theme
ii. The main point Sara is making ➔ _____ main point
iii. The findings of the authors ➔ the _____ findings
iv. The favorite writer of the people ➔ the _____ favorite writer

With the Bible in particular, **10** the printers' intentions were clear: these texts were meant to be preached, so the preachers would need clear indications of where to pause and how long to do so.

10. A) NO CHANGE
    B) the printers intentions
    C) the printer's intentions'
    D) the printers' intention's

What's changing in the answer choices?

_____

What is this question testing?

_____

Which of the two reasons can you cite to use an apostrophe?

_____

When you are using pronouns
- Possessives take NO apostrophes
- Contractions take apostrophes

Possessive Pronouns

- My
- His
- Her
- Their
- Its
- Whose

Pronoun Contractions

- I'm   (*I am*)
- He's   (*He is/He has*)
- She's   (*She is/She has*)
- They're   (*They are*)
- It's   (*It is/It has*)
- Who's   (*Who is/Who has*)

Rewrite the following examples as indicated using either possessive pronouns or contractions.

i.   The thesis statement belongs to him. ➔ The thesis statement is _____.

ii. The rights to the movie belong to us. ➔ The movie rights are _____.

iii. The essay's grammar is a mess. ➔ _____ grammar is a mess.

iv. The editors are going to need some extra time. ➔ _____ going to need some extra time.

v.   The credit for the idea all belongs to her. ➔ _____ all _____.

These indicators eventually became the punctuation marks that we use today, and **11** it's because of these little squiggles that writers can share their words with such a vast group of readers.

11. A) NO CHANGE

    B) its because of these little squiggles that writer's can share there words

    C) it's because of these little squiggle's that writers can share they're words

    D) it's because of these little squiggles that writers can share they're words

What's changing in the answer choices?

_____

What is this question testing?

_____

Which of the two reasons can you cite to use an apostrophe?

_____

THIS PAGE IS LEFT INTENTIONALLY BLANK.

DRILL

Time: 6 minutes

A Period History, Comma Get Some Knowledge, Part II

Punctuation had gained traction throughout the Middle **1** Ages, it was mainly *elocutionary* (for oral speech) rather than *syntactical* (for written speech). Ben Jonson's *English* **2** *Grammar*, written in 1617 but published in 1640, was among the first works to propose standard syntactical punctuation. The idea caught on **3** quickly, probably, because readers appreciated the new clarification that came with it. By the 1800s, though, the pendulum had swung too far the other way, and some **4** style manual's advised a comma usage that we would find distractingly overblown today.

1

A) NO CHANGE
B) Ages, but it
C) Ages but it
D) Ages. But it

2

A) NO CHANGE
B) *Grammar* written in 1617 but published in 1640
C) *Grammar*, written in 1617, but published in 1640,
D) *Grammar* written in 1617 but published in 1640,

3

A) NO CHANGE
B) quickly; probably
C) quickly. Probably,
D) quickly, probably

4

A) NO CHANGE
B) style manuals' advised
C) style manual's were advising
D) style manuals advised

Punctuation as we use it today is part of a movement that began in Britain in 1906, when the Fowler brothers, Henry Watson and Francis George, published **5** they're guide to *The Kings English*, which advised light punctuation. By that point, commas, semi-colons, **6** apostrophes, and colons had become so arcane that many of the newcomers to **7** literacy, such as those in the growing middle class, were intimidated and confused. It is because of the Fowlers that we now use punctuation only when we have a very good reason to do so, in a very limited and specific number of **8** instances. The fact that the period is much better known today than the semi-colon, along with the near death of "whom" and the subjunctive mood, is thanks to **9** the Fowler brothers handiwork.

5

A) NO CHANGE

B) they're guide to *The King's English*,

C) their guide to *The King's English*,

D) there guide to *The Kings English*,

6

A) NO CHANGE

B) apostrophes and colons

C) apostrophes, colons

D) apostrophes; and colons

7

A) NO CHANGE

B) literacy such as those in the growing middle class were intimidated and confused.

C) literacy such as those in the growing middle class, were intimidated, and confused.

D) literacy, such as those in the growing middle class, were intimidated, and confused.

8

Which of the following alternatives to the underlined portion would NOT be acceptable?

A) instances; the fact

B) instances: the fact

C) instances, the fact

D) instances—the fact

9

A) NO CHANGE

B) the Fowler brothers' handiwork.

C) the Fowler brother's handiwork.

D) the Fowler brothers's handiwork.

American English has followed much the same course as British **10** English. Though the strictest grammar treatises tend to come from American sources. Such grammatical precision (what many would call pedantry) is nowhere more on display than in the makeup of the college-admissions standardized tests, each of which measures **11** it's many test-takers abilities to follow such rules.

10

A) NO CHANGE
B) English; though
C) English, but though,
D) English though

11

A) NO CHANGE
B) it's many test-takers'
C) their many test-takers'
D) its many test-takers'

Summary

- How can the answer choices tell you what a question is testing?

  _____

  _____

- What kinds of punctuation can come between two ideas?

  _____

  _____

- Why are the colon and the long-dash referred to as "Half-Stop" punctuation?

  _____

  _____

- What are the four reasons to use a comma on the SAT?

  _____

  _____

  _____

  _____

- What should you do if you can't cite a reason to use a comma or an apostrophe?

  _____

  _____

- I have accomplished _____ of the _____ goals stated in the Introduction chapter.

| **109**

WORDS

"The difference between the almost-right word and
the right word is really a large matter—
it's the difference between the lightning-bug and the lightning."

—Mark Twain

Goals Review

At the conclusion of this chapter, you will have mastered the following:

- Apply the basic approach to questions dealing with words.
- Know how to keep verbs consistent with other verbs within a passage.
- Make nouns and pronouns consistent with one another and as precise as possible.
- Recognize and select the most concise answers.

CONSISTENCY, PRECISION, AND CONCISION

With 44 questions, the SAT could test any number of grammar concepts, from the universally known to the completely obscure. We'll talk about some of SAT's favorites here, but we'll do so under three particular headings.

- The correct choice is *Consistent* with the rest of the sentence and passage.
- The correct choice features words and phrases that are as *Precise* as possible.
- The correct choice, free of any errors, will be the most *Concise*.

In this chapter, we'll focus on how these three rules apply to different words, especially nouns, pronouns, and verbs. In general, however, just remember this:

Once you've checked the answers, name the mistakes and use POE.

CONSISTENCY IS KEY

The history of the English language is a curious one. Historians of the language **1** identifies three categories: Old English (450-1100), Middle English (1100-1500), and Modern English (1500-present).

1. A) NO CHANGE
   B) is identified
   C) identify
   D) are identified

What's changing in the answer choices?

_____

What is this question testing?

_____

By this point, Old and Middle English are essentially dead languages, and the great texts of those eras, such as *Beowulf* or *The Canterbury Tales*, **2** were translated into Modern English.

2. A) NO CHANGE
   B) are translated
   C) translated
   D) has been translated

What's changing in the answer choices?

_____

What is this question testing?

_____

Let the non-underlined portions guide your choice of verbs. Verbs need to be consistent in number with their subjects and consistent in tense and form with other verbs.

READING

WRITING AND LANGUAGE

MATH

ESSAY

Looking at these transformations [3] show that every time we read or speak English, we are giving voice to over 1,500 years of history.

3. A) NO CHANGE

B) show that every time we read or speak the English language, we are giving voice

C) shows that every time we read or spoke the English language, we have been giving voice

D) shows that every time we read or speak English, we give voice

What's changing in the answer choices?

_____

What is this question testing?

_____

Now among the 360 million native speakers of English, the differences in [4] our dialect and country of origin show the living history.

4. A) NO CHANGE

B) our dialects and countries of origin show

C) our dialects and countries of origin shows

D) our dialect's and country's of origin show

What's changing in the answer choices?

_____

What is this question testing?

_____

When Julius Caesar's army landed on British shores in 55 BCE, neither his language [5] nor the local inhabitants bore any relation to what would eventually become English.

5. A) NO CHANGE

B) nor those, of the local inhabitants

C) nor that of the local inhabitants

D) nor the inhabitants language

What's changing in the answer choices?

_____

What is this question testing?

_____

Like Verbs, Nouns and Pronouns must be consistent with the non-underlined portions of the sentence.

Find the partner!

- For Verbs, find the subject and the other verbs.
- For Nouns, find the other nouns.
- For Pronouns, find the other pronouns and nouns.

SAT has lots of names for these different concepts: verb tense and mood, noun agreement, parallel structure, logical comparison, and pronoun agreement. What do all of these names have in common? Consistency!

Caesar's Roman armies spoke Latin, and the British natives spoke Celtish, a variety of which is now present in Irish Gaelic. "Old English" came instead with **6** the Germanic tribes and its languages during the tribes' invasion in the 5th century.

6. A) NO CHANGE
   B) the Germanic tribes and they're languages
   C) the Germanic tribes and their languages
   D) tribes and their languages

What's changing in the answer choices?

_____

What is this question testing?

_____

PRECISION IS BETTER THAN, LIKE, WHATEVER

In fact, **7** it comes from one of them, the Angles, from modern-day Denmark, whose "Angle Land" became "Engel Land" and "England."

7. A) NO CHANGE

   B) the name "English" comes from one of those tribes,

   C) "English" as a name comes from one of them,

   D) the name "English" is a gift given by one of them,

What's changing in the answer choices?

_____

What is this question testing?

_____

Once you are sure that a word or phrase is consistent with the non-underlined portions, make that word or phrase as precise as you can.

A Pro Now at Pronouns

Pronouns are some of the most misused parts of speech in the English language. In the exercise below, make sure the pronouns are consistent with the non-underlined portions, and if the pronouns are not precise enough, replace them with something better.

    i.   The main Germanic invaders of Britain were the Angles, Saxons, and Jutes. "Anglo-Saxon" is a term many people know, but <u>they</u> are mostly forgotten.

    ii.   Every English speaker can understand a little bit of German because of <u>their</u> similarity.

    iii.   Refined diction and near-perfect grammar can be learned, but <u>it's</u> also very easy to forget.

    iv.   Each of us uses some Germanic words in <u>their</u> everyday speech.

    v.   The Internet, Twitter, and Facebook may be as influential on the history and the language as the Norman Conquest was on <u>it</u> in 1066.

According to one study, approximately [8] <u>26% come</u> from this Germanic influence.

8. A) NO CHANGE
   B) 26% of modern English
   C) 26% of modern English words
   D) twenty-six percent

What's changing in the answer choices?

_____

What is this question testing?

_____

Still, Old English is a foreign language, and those who want to read *Beowulf* in the original must learn Old English as they would any other foreign language. In fact, our [9] <u>contemporary knowledge comes to us of Old English through Latin</u> and the scribbled translations of scholars and monks who were fluent in both languages.

9. A) NO CHANGE
   B) contemporary knowledge comes to us through Latin of Old English
   C) contemporary English knowledge of Old comes to us through Latin
   D) contemporary knowledge of Old English comes to us through Latin

What's changing in the answer choices?

_____

What is this question testing?

_____

Modifier Modifications

Underline the misplaced modifiers in each of these sentences. Move the modifier or rewrite the sentences as necessary.

i. Studying for six weeks, a reading knowledge of Old English can be acquired.

ii. Once acquired, you can read *Beowulf* and other texts with the aid of a dictionary.

iii. If you'd rather not learn a new language, there are some wonderful versions of old texts by accomplished translators in Modern English.

iv. I first saw Seamus Heaney's translation of *Beowulf* with a friend in college at a bookstore

v. Obsolete and frankly a little dull, I opted out of the Old English class.

MAKING THE FINAL CONCISIONS

Once you've eliminated all the grammatical errors, pick the shortest remaining answer.

Middle English is a different story, as it bears a
10 closer resemblance to the language that you are reading right now.

10. A) NO CHANGE
    B) very much closer
    C) altogether closer and nearer
    D) much more close

What's changing in the answer choices?

_____

What is this question testing?

_____

Modern English may be 26% Germanic, but a much larger portion of it comes from the **11** Normans, who were also major contributors.

11. A) NO CHANGE
    B) Normans, who did their own fair share of contributing.
    C) Normans, who were no slouches in the contribution department.
    D) Normans.

What's changing in the answer choices?

_____

What is this question testing?

_____

When SAT is testing *words*, make sure that those words are

- **Consistent.** Verbs, nouns, and pronouns should agree within sentences and passages.
- **Precise.** Make sure the writing communicates specific ideas and events.
- **Concise.** Pick the answer that does the most work in the fewest words.

DRILL

Time: 8 minutes

The Story of English, as told by… English

The Norman Conquest took place in 1066 and **1** is led by William the Conqueror of Normandy, part of modern-day France. With the Norman Conquest came an influx of a new language, French. At first, Norman French was the language of only the royal court and upper classes, but by 1362 **2** it had been established as the language of law, as it was the language used to conduct parliamentary debates. Only fifteen years earlier, English had replaced Latin as the primary language of **3** instruction. By the end of the 14th century, Geoffrey Chaucer would begin to write his *Canterbury Tales*, still the gold standard of Middle-English works of literature. Such a work might still be difficult for modern readers, but it is not the illegible text that **4** Old English would be.

1

A) NO CHANGE
B) is leading
C) was led
D) were led

2

A) NO CHANGE
B) English had
C) it was
D) they had

3

A) NO CHANGE
B) instruction, to the detriment of Latin.
C) instruction, having replaced the Latin language.
D) instruction, instead of Latin.

4

A) NO CHANGE
B) the Old English
C) a comparable work in Old English
D) the language of Old English

Although English was spoken all over the British Isles, Middle English had never become a fully standardized written language. Such standardization **5** comes after a technological innovation, the printing press, meant that readers far and wide could read the same texts. Now that readers were looking **6** all over England at the same texts, the regional dialects that dispersed Middle English could no longer stand. Since London was the center of population and intellectual life, **7** their dialect became the closest thing the English had to an "official" language, and its speakers, those such as William Shakespeare, Ben Jonson, and later John Milton, **8** was read so far and wide that enjoying their works, or reaching a broad audience of one's own, meant working in that particular dialect of English.

5

A) NO CHANGE
B) had come
C) will have come
D) would come

6

The best placement for the underlined portion would be
A) where it is now.
B) after the word *readers*.
C) after the word *regional*.
D) after the word *stand* (and before the period).

7

A) NO CHANGE
B) there
C) it's
D) its

8

A) NO CHANGE
B) was reading
C) were reading
D) were read

The attempts to standardize English spelling and grammar intensified during the 17th and 18th centuries, culminating in the three major dictionaries of the eighteenth and nineteenth centuries: Samuel Johnson's *Dictionary of the English Language*, first published in 1755; **9** Noah Webster's work in the *American Dictionary of the English Language*, first published in 1828, and The Philological Society of London's *Oxford English Dictionary*, first published in 1884.

Still, however authoritative these works may be, English continues to evolve. American English, for instance, has been influenced by its contact with Spanish colonists and Native Americans. British English has been influenced by its proximity to Europe and by its history as a major colonial empire. Establishing English footholds in South Africa and **10** setting them up in India may have forced English on the colonized peoples, but the English language could not be unaffected. English is a living language, and its history is living history, regardless of any attempts to halt **11** such constant transformation.

9
A) NO CHANGE
B) Noah Webster's *American Dictionary of the English Language*, first published in 1828;
C) the *American Dictionary of the English Language* (1828), conceived by Noah Webster,
D) Noah Webster's 1828 first edition of the *American Dictionary of the English Language*;

10
A) NO CHANGE
B) India
C) also establishing them in India
D) India, too,

11
A) NO CHANGE
B) it.
C) them.
D) us.

Summary

- If verbs are changing in the answer choices, keep those verbs consistent with…

  _____

  _____

- If nouns are changing in the answer choices, keep those nouns consistent with…

  _____

  _____

- If pronouns are changing in the answer choices, keep those pronouns consistent with…

  _____

  _____

- On the SAT, a specific noun is often better than a pronoun because the specific noun is more…

  _____

  _____

- When all grammatical errors are eliminated, choose the _____ answer.

  _____

  _____

- I have accomplished _____ of the _____ goals stated in the Introduction chapter.

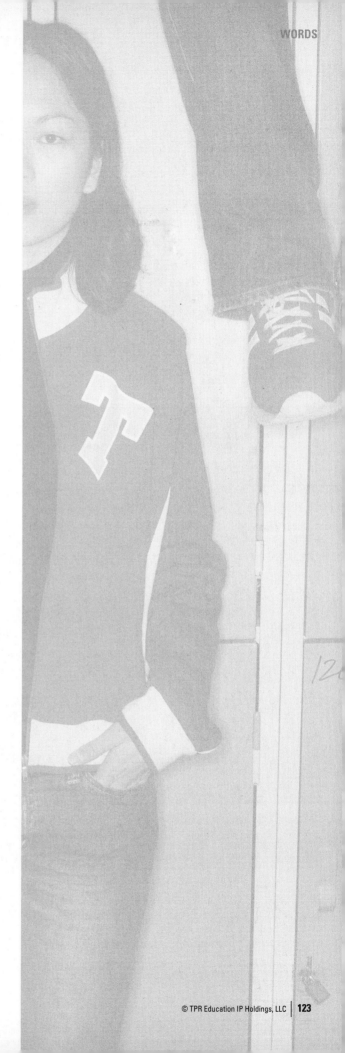

QUESTIONS

REVIEW EXERCISE

The form of English continues to change before our very eyes. **1** The history of the language seems to be that of the incorporation of various foreign languages, today **2** it is a much more local one. Now **3** the words of business and technological slang are becoming the common currency of the English language. The writers of the SAT, for instance, have discarded the obscure vocabulary words of literature and history in favor of a more practical set, those that a student **4** was likely to hear in **5** the "real world" of employment, which is to say, the workforce.

1. A) NO CHANGE
   B) However, the
   C) Because the
   D) Although the

2. A) NO CHANGE
   B) the change
   C) one
   D) DELETE the underlined portion.

3. A) NO CHANGE
   B) the words, of business and technological slang, are
   C) the word's of business and technological slang, are
   D) the words, of business, and technological, slang, are

4. A) NO CHANGE
   B) were
   C) had been
   D) might be

5. A) NO CHANGE
   B) the "real world" of work,
   C) the "real world" of a 9-to-5er, maybe,
   D) the "real world,"

SAT makes a big deal about the separation between Expression of Ideas and Standard English Conventions. Three of the questions above fit into one category and two fit into the other. Is there really such a difference? We don't think so.

There are some questions that do require a bit of a different approach, however, and we're going to look at those in this chapter.

Goals Review

At the conclusion of this chapter, you will have mastered the following:

- Adapt the basic approach to problems that ask specific questions.
- Learn the types of questions that will be asked in the W&L section.
- Answer questions as literally and precisely as possible.
- Find answers and information that are consistent with other parts of the passage.

QUESTIONS

Nearly all of the questions we've seen so far have been Proofreader questions, or those that fix particular errors within a passage. In this chapter, we'll look at the other type, Editor questions, which ask for some different things. The biggest difference between these two types of questions is that Editor questions actually *ask*. Make sure you read the questions they ask carefully!

The most important thing about questions on the Writing and Language Test is to notice them.

WORDS AND PUNCTUATION WITH A CATCH

Some of the Editor questions on the SAT will test the same concepts we saw in earlier chapters. Make sure to read these questions carefully so as not to fall into one of SAT's traps.

Education provides the answers. This idea is so obvious that it seemingly doesn't require any **1** explanation, and current educational trends toward math and sciences would seem to bear it out.

1. Which of the following alternatives to the underlined portion would NOT be acceptable?
   A) explanation; current
   B) explanation, as current
   C) explanation, current
   D) explanation—current

   What's changing in the answer choices?

   _____

   What is this question testing?

   _____

   What technique can you use?

   _____

We would not be wrong to **2** wonder, however, whether this emphasis on answers has made good on its promise.

2. All of the following alternatives to the underlined portion would be acceptable EXCEPT
   A) awe
   B) question
   C) ponder
   D) weigh

   Which of these words is *consistent* with the meaning given in the original sentence?

   _____

   What word is left? That's your answer.

   _____

On EXCEPT/LEAST/NOT questions, the sentence is correct as written. Use the correct sentence to single out the incorrect answer choice.

More people than ever are attending colleges and universities. The fact that there are more people attending colleges and universities lets us ask, what do people learn there? **3**

3. Which of the following gives the best way to combine these two sentences?

A) More people than ever are attending colleges and universities; the fact that there are more people attending colleges and universities lets us ask, what do people learn there?

B) More people than ever are attending colleges and universities, which raises the question, what do people learn there?

C) More people than ever are attending colleges and universities: this fact of more attendance asks a question, what do people learn there?

D) More people than ever are attending colleges and universities. What do people learn there?

Which is the most *concise?*

_____

Does it fit the parameters of the question?

_____

PRECISE QUESTIONS

As we discussed in the last chapter, the best answers on the SAT are often the most *precise*. That is just as true for the Editor questions as it is for the Proofreader questions.

Answer the question in the most precise way possible.
Read literally!

This question is too big to answer in this short essay, but the fact that we cannot answer it here should encourage us. 4

Perhaps the *answers* are less important in university education than are the *questions*. 5 After all, if a student enters and leaves college with the same amount of certainty, why go to school at all?

4. The writer is considering deleting the phrase *in this short essay* from the preceding sentence and adjusting the punctuation accordingly. Should this phrase be kept or deleted?

A) Kept, because removing it would change the meaning of this part of the sentence.

B) Kept, because it reminds the reader of the length of this particular text.

C) Deleted, because it wrongly implies that the question could be answered in a longer text.

D) Deleted, because it gives information that has no bearing on this particular text.

5. At this point, the writer is considering adding the following true statement:

Questions are typically punctuated with the mark ?, much like the one at the end of the next sentence.

Should the writer make this addition here?

A) Yes, because it clarifies the grammatical structure of the passage as a whole.

B) Yes, because it shows that the writer has authority on what is being described.

C) No, because it does not contribute in a significant way to the main point of the paragraph.

D) No, because questions are often implied without the help of question marks.

On "proposition" questions, make sure the word or phrase has some precise and definable role within the sentence or passage.

6 There is no question that e-books may replace paper books altogether in a few years. All the books one reads in college are available to non-students, so it should be the role of universities and professors to show students the larger implications of those books and ideas. The questions generated by the big ideas can help to clarify the purpose of students' own lives. Students can discover their passions and articulate the reasons that those passions might matter to the world. Students can overcome their prejudices and presuppositions by wondering how they came to have those prejudices in the first place. **7**

6. Which of the following would best introduce the main subject of this paragraph?

A) NO CHANGE

B) Questions give students the material to think beyond the classroom and beyond their own lives.

C) The number of majors in the humanities has declined sharply since the 1960s.

D) I mean, seriously, *here's* a question: who reads a book anymore?

7. The writer wants to insert an idea that will support the idea given in the previous sentence ("Students... place"). Which of the following true statements would offer that support?

A) The United States has made leaps and bounds in eradicating prejudice, but there is still work to be done.

B) Prejudice has many sources, and all of them should be overcome in college.

C) Racial and gender prejudice can never be fully eliminated, as evidenced by some unfortunate contemporary events.

D) It is difficult to imagine someone holding on to an outdated intolerance after reading Frederick Douglass's beautiful and tragic narrative of his life as a slave.

CONSISTENCY QUESTIONS

As you may have noticed, Precision and Consistency are often intertwined. A major part of ensuring the precision and relevance of ideas has to do with how consistent those ideas are with what is being discussed.

Writing and Language passages should be judged on what they *do* say, not on what they *could* say. When dealing with Style, Tone, and Focus, make sure to work with the words and phrases the passage has already used.

[1] As any philosophy professor will tell you, the great legacy of "the question" is that of the Greek philosopher Socrates, particularly as he has been related to us in the writings of Plato. [2] Plato's famous work, *The Republic*, is a collection of such dialogues. [3] When Alfred North Whitehead declares that "all philosophy is a footnote to Plato," he refers to exactly this legacy of questioning. [4] Socrates began with the idea that his knowledge told him only that he knew nothing. [5] His intense questioning is captured in a series of dialogues with fellow Athenians. 8

8. The best placement for Sentence 2 would be
   A) where it is now.
   B) after sentence 3.
   C) after sentence 4.
   D) after sentence 5.

What Socrates showed to everyone with whom he spoke, and to everyone who now reads his conversations, was that everything is an open question. Such an approach can help with the big abstract questions of all lives, **9** but people who don't care about the big questions don't really need to read it. As a result, the quality of university life is much higher when Socrates is placed rightfully at the center of it. It is well known that the **10** early 1930s was a moment of crisis or war in America, and we cannot help but notice an attendant reduction in mentions of Socrates in American universities. In the end, it seems that the soul of inquisitive and self-conscious life is Socrates. So what was it about him that made his influence so powerful and all-encompassing? **11** Well, as Socrates himself might say, that's a good question.

9. Which of the following choices would best contrast with the idea presented in the first part of the sentence?
A) NO CHANGE
B) though many philosophers have given more pragmatic approaches to living.
C) but it applies just as much to the smaller questions of a single life.
D) although this persistent line of questioning can become very frustrating.

10. Which choice gives information consistent with the graph?
A) NO CHANGE
B) 1910s and 1970s were moments
C) late 1920s was a moment
D) 1930s and 1950s were moments

11. Which of the following would best conclude the essay by preserving its style and tone?
A) NO CHANGE
B) It was probably Plato's eloquent retelling of Socrates's life.
C) Stodgy philosophy professors seriously make you read so much boring stuff.
D) It's odd given that Aristotle's range of topics was so much broader.

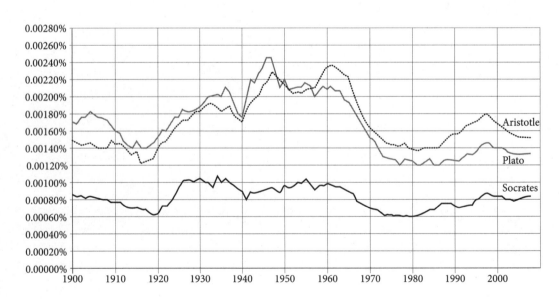

CHARTS AND GRAPHS

It may seem a little odd to have charts attached to Writing and Language passages, but don't worry. The task for these is the same as it is for anything else on this section: keep your answers *consistent* with the graphs and as *precise* as possible. Oftentimes, you don't even need the passage to answer these questions.

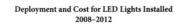

Deployment and Cost for LED Lights Installed
2008–2012

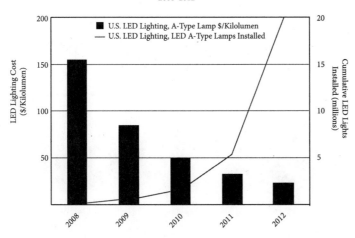

i. Which of the following gives information consistent with the graph?

A) the price of lighting the average home has skyrocketed since 2008.

B) LED bulbs are proven to be better for the environment.

C) an increase in LED bulb usage has led to a significant reduction in cost.

D) certain types of bulbs have become much more expensive while some have become cheaper.

READING

WRITING AND LANGUAGE

MATH

ESSAY

Annual Greenhouse Gas Emissions by Sector

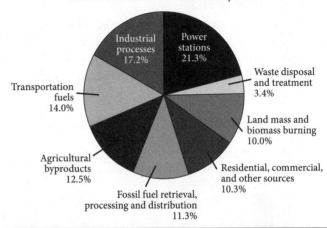

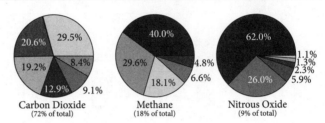

Carbon Dioxide
(72% of total)

Methane
(18% of total)

Nitrous Oxide
(9% of total)

ii. Which of the following gives information consistent with the chart?

A) Power stations are accountable for nearly half of all greenhouse gas emissions.

B) Agricultural byproducts make up less than a tenth of all greenhouse gas emissions.

C) Greenhouse-gas emissions from waste disposal are greater than those from industrial processes.

D) Transportation fuels and industrial processes together account for more than a quarter of all greenhouse-gas emissions.

Check the answer choices against the graphs. Make sure that information is consistent with both the passage and the figure.

DRILL

Time: 10 minutes

The Socratic Problem to the Socratic Method

[1] Teacher of Crito and Alcibiades, Socrates the man has been elusive to modern historians. The "Socratic problem," as it is known, has [2] challenged historians and philosophers for many centuries. Socrates himself wrote nothing that survives, and his biographical details are sparse when even the most prominent citizen's deeds were recorded on a loose time scale. [3] All that we know about Socrates comes from three sources: the philosophical writings of Plato and Xenophon and the plays of Aristophanes. All three agree that there was a philosophizing man of such a name, but they agree on little else.

1

Which of the following choices would best introduce the essay by contrasting Socrates's intellectual legacy with the other topics discussed in this paragraph?

A) NO CHANGE

B) An Athenian born amid historical transformation,

C) Despite his central role in modern thought,

D) Although his name is often mispronounced,

2

Which of the following alternatives to the underlined portion would be LEAST acceptable?

A) baffled

B) confounded

C) perplexed

D) battled

3

The writer is considering deleting the phrase *on a loose time scale* from the preceding sentence, placing the period after the word *recorded*. Should the phrase be kept or deleted?

A) Kept, because it reminds readers that even historians are imperfect people.

B) Kept, because the sentence contains the opposite meaning without this phrase.

C) Deleted, because sentences should be made more concise whenever possible.

D) Deleted, because it contains information already given elsewhere in the passage.

[1] It is generally agreed that Socrates was born in Athens in 470 or 469 BCE, **4** approximately 400 years before the birth of the Roman emperor Caesar Augustus. [2] His father was a sculptor, and his mother was a midwife. Socrates eventually married Xanthippe, with whom he had three sons. Socrates's father cut stone for the **5** Parthenon, and Socrates, having learned his father's trade, initially earned his living as a stonecutter. [3] After his retirement from stonecutting, however, Socrates began his life's great work. [4] His life's great work consisted of discussing philosophy. **6** [5] Regardless of whether he was paid or not, this teaching, and its supposed "corruption of the young," ultimately contributed to the philosopher's death sentence by an Athenian court. [6] The plays of Aristophanes suggest that Socrates was paid for his philosophical teaching of the young, though Plato's account of Socrates's final words disagrees with such an idea. **7**

500 BC   400 BC   300 BC   200 BC   100 BC

ALEXANDER THE GREAT ⊢356–323⊣
PLATO ⊢427–327⊣
SCIPIO (Elder) ⊢236–184⊣
JULIUS CAESAR ⊢100–44⊣
SOCRATES ⊢470–399⊣
ARISTOTLE ⊢384–322⊣
ZENO ⊢335–263⊣
AUGUSTUS CAESAR ⊢63BC–14 AD⊣
CICERO ⊢106–43⊣
THE NATION OF ISRAEL
⊢ PERSIAN DOMINATION ⊢ GREEK DOMINATION ⊢ ⊢MACCABEAN RULE⊣ ⊢ ROME⊣
EZRA ⊢458–390⊣
Book of Enoch
Book of Daniel
PHILO ⊢20BC–50AD
I Maccabees

4

Which of the following choices gives information consistent with the figure?

A) NO CHANGE

B) after Aristotle's great philosophical discoveries.

C) amid the era of Greek domination.

D) around the time the Jewish Book of Enoch was written.

5

Which of the following alternatives to the underlined portion would NOT be acceptable?

A) Parthenon, then, Socrates,

B) Parthenon. Then, Socrates,

C) Parthenon; Socrates,

D) Parthenon; thus, Socrates,

6

Which of the following gives the most effective way to combine sentences 3 and 4, reproduced below?

After his retirement from stonecutting, however, Socrates began his life's great work. His life's great work consisted of discussing philosophy.

A) (keep the sentences as they are)

B) After his retirement from stonecutting, however, Socrates began his life's great work; that great work consisted of discussing philosophy.

C) After his retirement from stonecutting, however Socrates began his life's great work: discussing philosophy.

D) After the stonecutting retirement, Socrates, however, began his life's great work, which consisted of the discussion of philosophy.

7

The best placement for sentence 6 would be

A) where it is now.

B) before sentence 1.

C) before sentence 2.

D) before sentence 5.

Socrates makes a few appearances in the military and political history of his era. **8** He was a soldier in the Athenian army during three notable campaigns, and he eventually played a role in government, most notably in the defense of Athenian generals who abandoned their dead in the water in order to continue to pursue the Spartan navy. Political life at this time was in transition. **9** Socrates clashed with Athenian authorities over how the defeated province should govern itself.

8

At this point, the author is considering adding the following true statement

> Thucydides's classic work, *A History of the Peloponnesian War*, is an excellent source on this era's military history.

Should the writer make the addition here?

A) Yes, because it adds weight to an essay that lacks historical validity.

B) Yes, because it names one of the greatest works of the man being discussed.

C) No, because it strays from the paragraph's focus on the life of Socrates.

D) No, because it cites a text that is too old to be considered historically reliable.

9

The writer wants to insert an idea that will support the idea given in the previous sentence ("Political… transition"). Which of the following statements would offer that support?

A) Governments frequently go through such transitions, though they are not always so intolerant of dissent.

B) That doesn't excuse the fact that the Athenians executed such a great man.

C) The powerful Athenians had recently been defeated by the Spartans in the Peloponnesian War.

D) Athens is known fondly as the "school of Greece," because it produced so many great minds.

READING

WRITING AND
LANGUAGE

MATH

ESSAY

10 For most of his life, Socrates was an average, if at times controversial, citizen. His greatest contributions came late in life as a philosopher. His great contribution to the future of philosophy and instruction, particularly by some of the most adept test-preparation teachers in the world, was that of the Socratic method. The method broke any problem down into a series of questions, or testable hypotheses. Those discussing the topic would question it tirelessly, discarding hypotheses that could not stand up to reasonable questioning. It was from this method that Plato and Xenophon built their own philosophies, using Socrates as the mouthpiece. Even more, however, it was from this method that the system of Western knowledge production was built, and why, for everything from the sciences to the humanities, the history of knowledge in the West is one of thesis, antithesis, and synthesis. **11**

10

Which of the following choices would offer the most effective transition between the previous paragraph and the current one?

A) NO CHANGE

B) His political views rarely won the day, and they sometimes got him in trouble.

C) Socrates has a wonderful cameo in the movie *Bill and Ted's Excellent Adventure*.

D) No one's really sure whether *The Republic* is filled with Plato's ideas or Socrates's ideas.

11

The writer is considering replacing the word *knowledge* in the preceding sentence with the word *brains*. Should the writer make the change or keep the sentence as it is?

A) Make the change, because it identifies the part of the body being discussed.

B) Make the change, because it creates a surreal image of brains literally speaking to one another.

C) Keep the sentence as it is, because the original sentence uses a more sophisticated-sounding word to describe the same thing.

D) Keep the sentence as it is, because the original sentence features a more precise word in keeping with the rest of the paragraph.

Summary

- The most important thing about questions on the W&L section is

  _____ .

- When you see EXCEPT, LEAST, or NOT in a question, you should

  _____ .

- When adding information to a passage, you should make sure that information is _____ with other information from the passage and as _____ as possible.

- The Writing and Language Test is different from the Reading Test in that

  _____

  _____ .

- I have accomplished _____ of the _____ goals stated at the beginning of this chapter.

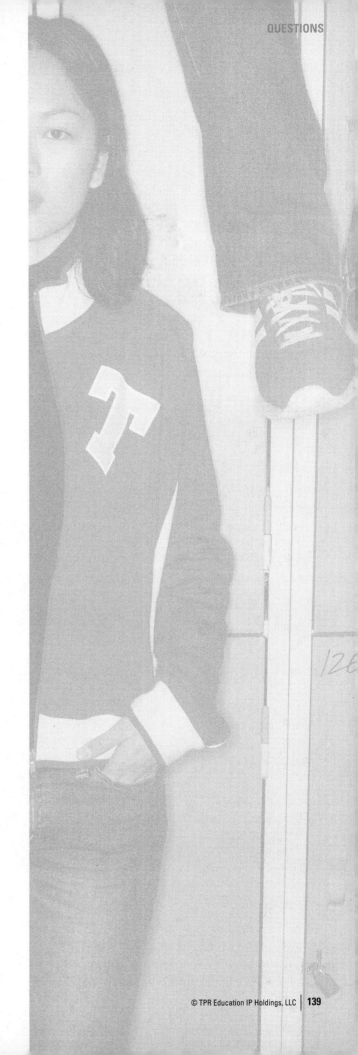

MATH

Yes Calculator

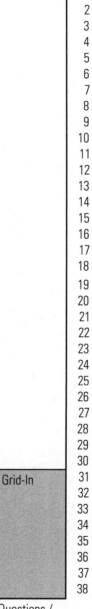

1
2
3
4
5
6
7
8
9
10
11
12
13
14
15
16
17
18
19
20
21
22
23
24
25
26
27
28
29
30

Grid-In

31
32
33
34
35
36
37
38

38 Questions /
55 minutes

No Calculator

1
2
3
4
5
6
7
8
9
10
11
12
13
14
15

Grid-In

16
17
18
19
20

20 Questions /
25 minutes

GLOBAL TECHNIQUES

"Not everything that counts can be counted.
Not everything that can be counted counts."

–William Bruce Cameron

READING

WRITING AND
LANGUAGE

MATH

ESSAY

Attacking a Project

When you have a large project for school, say a 10-page paper or a 10-minute speech, you can't simply sit down and do everything from start to finish. Instead, you have to break down the project and determine how to go about attacking the project. What sorts of ways have you broken up projects in the past, and how do you decide where to start?

Goals Review

At the conclusion of this chapter, you will be able to accomplish the following:

- Understand *how* to decide which questions to do in the Math sections
- Understand *how* and *when* to eliminate answers and to guess
- Understand *how* to slow down to improve accuracy
- Understand *how* to use your calculator wisely

READING

WRITING AND LANGUAGE

MATH

ESSAY

SCORING

Believe it or not, there are things you can do right now before learning anything else about math that can improve your score. Small changes to the number and type of questions you attempt can have a huge impact on your score. The following strategies will help you throughout the test. The best place to start is with a score improvement goal.

Practice Test B GOALS

Practice Test A Math score: _____

Practice Test B Math goal: _____

Aim for 20 points above your Test A Math score. Refer back to your goals after each diagnostic test; as your score goes up, increase your goal score as well. Unless you are already scoring a 750 or higher, **don't** do every question!

Slow down. Choose questions wisely, and spend enough time on them to get them right.

Don't give away points by making careless errors.

POOD

So how do you know which questions to do and which ones to skip? Make sure to follow your POOD, and focus on these two ideas.

Do questions that can be answered quickly and accurately.

Do questions that can be made easier using TPR strategies.

LEVELS OF DIFFICULTY

Throughout the first 3 chapters of this book, levels of difficulty are indicated in the margin next to each question. These reflect the difficulty of the question as ETS sees it, not how easy it will be for each student. First and foremost, make sure to tackle questions in your POOD. To force you to do that, the Levels of Difficulty indicators will not appear in the last 4 math chapters. It's up to you to decide which questions to do and which to skip.

POE

Throughout this intro, and throughout the Math sections, look for opportunities to use POE. There are more wrong answers than right ones. When you find a wrong answer, cross it off!

GUESSING AND PACING

Remember to guess on any questions that you don't get to legitimately complete. There is no penalty for wrong answers, so try to get some of the questions right by guessing. Just make sure to always guess the same letter, your Letter of the Day (LOTD), to increase the odds of getting some of them right!

R.T.F.Q.

ETS will often ask for something unexpected in a question and will, of course, have trap answers that would result from misreading or miscalculating. Read the full question carefully, and underline the key words before doing any calculations.

What would you do if your Math teacher asked you to solve these questions?

If $-\dfrac{3}{2} < 2x - 5 < -1$, then _____?

If $x = \dfrac{51}{x+14}$, then _____?

Now look at these SAT questions.

34. If $-\dfrac{3}{2} < 2x - 5 < -1$, what is one possible value of $-4x + 10$?

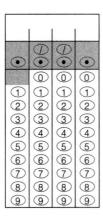

Difficulty: Medium

8. If $x = \dfrac{51}{x + 14}$, which of the following could be the value of $x^2 + 5$?

A)   3

B)   19

C)   56

D)   294

Difficulty: Medium

Always make sure to

R_____

T_____

F_____

Q_____

Unnecessary information may appear in the question. Focus only on what you need to get the answer as efficiently as possible.

BITE-SIZED PIECES

Don't be overwhelmed by long, seemingly complicated problems. Look for ways to take shortcuts on complicated plug-and-chug questions. For wordy word problems, read carefully, and attack them one step at a time. Either jot down notes as you read or solve as you go, so you don't have to keep track of too much in your head.

Work questions one small step at a time. Start with whatever piece makes the most sense to you. Look for opportunities to use POE.

Difficulty: Medium

What's $8n^3 + 21n^3$?

How does knowing the answer help with POE?

6. $2(4n^3 - 2n^2 + n + 8) - 3(-7n^3 + 2n^2 - 5n + 9) =$

A) $-13n^3 + 10n^2 - 17n + 11$

B) $-13n^3 - 10n^2 + 17n - 11$

C) $29n^3 + 10n^2 - 17n + 11$

D) $29n^3 - 10n^2 + 17n - 11$

Difficulty: Medium

What's $\left(8^{\frac{2}{3}}\right)^3$?

How does knowing the answer help with POE?

18. $\left(8^{\frac{2}{3}} x^4 y^7 z^2\right)^3$ can be simplified to which of the following expressions?

A) $16x^7y^{10}z^5$

B) $16x^{12}y^{21}z^6$

C) $64x^7y^{10}z^5$

D) $64x^{12}y^{21}z^6$

9. Chinua is selling lemonade at a stand in front of his home. Each day, Chinua's net profit or loss on sales of lemonade after deducting the cost of supplies and ingredients is equal to $0.50g – $15, where g represents the number of glasses of lemonade sold that day. If Chinua sold 50 glasses of lemonade on Monday, 20 glasses of lemonade on Tuesday, and 60 glasses of lemonade on Wednesday, which of the following expresses Chinua's total net profit, in dollars, over all three days?

A) 20

B) 30

C) 40

D) 50

Difficulty: Medium
What's the best place to start—finding the net profit for Monday or finding the total number of glasses sold?

10. Natalia is joining an online music service that charges a monthly membership fee of $5.95. A tax of 9% is applied to the monthly membership fee, and an additional one-time initiation fee of $15 is charged at the beginning of the membership. Which of the following represents Natalia's total charge, in dollars, for a membership lasting m months?

A) $1.09(5.95m + 15)$

B) $1.09(5.95m) + 15$

C) $1.09m(5.95 + 15)$

D) $0.09m(5.95) + 15$

Difficulty: Medium
When does the $15 fee come into play? How does that help with POE?

POE POINT—By using POE each step of the way, you can sometimes get to the correct answer without completely solving the problem!

CALCULATOR USE

Some of the preceding questions were accompanied by a calculator symbol, and some were not. ETS has decided to see how students will fare if they are not allowed to use their calculators on one section. Crikey! The questions in this section can still be in your POOD, and TPR techniques will make many of them fairly straight-forward.

Whether calculator use is allowed or not, always make sure to

1. Read the question.
2. Set up the problem.

Only pick up your calculator after you've made sure to RTFQ and set the problem up on paper.

Difficulty: Medium

When using a calculator, follow the rules of PEMDAS!

P _____
E _____
M _____
D _____
A _____
S _____

33. If $f(x) = 14x + 5[6 - (2x + 3)]^2$, what is the value of $f(-2)$?

Even the questions that allow calculator usage are often written so that using it may actually end up being less effective or efficient.

BALLPARKING AND ESTIMATING

By determining what size answer you need before you begin calculating, you may be able to eliminate one or more answer choices. It will help you avoid falling into traps and improve your odds if you end up needing to guess. In particular, POE by Ballparking or Estimating is even more important when calculator use is not allowed.

If possible, eliminate answer choices that can't possibly be correct before calculating anything.

$$x^2 + y^2 = 125$$
$$y = -2x$$

11. If (x, y) is a solution to the system of equations above, what is the positive value of x ?

A) -5

B) 5

C) 10

D) 25

Difficulty: Medium

Rounding the numbers in the question to estimate your answer can also help save time. Don't multiply out awkward numbers on paper if you can use estimation.

2. If $\dfrac{x}{9} + \dfrac{2}{9} = 31$, then what is the value of $x + 2$?

A) 31

B) 93

C) 279

D) 648

Difficulty: Easy
Round awkward numbers to a close value that is easier to work with.

Summary

- By **slowing down**, I can _____.

- What questions should you focus on in the Math sections?

  _____

  _____

- When should you **guess** on a Math question?

  _____

- What does **R.T.F.Q.** stand for?

  _____

- What does that mean?

  _____

- What does it mean to take **Bite-Sized Pieces**?

  _____

- When do you use Bite-Sized Pieces?

  _____

- What is important to keep in mind about **calculator use**?

  _____

  _____

- What are **Ballparking** and **Estimation**?

  _____

  _____

- What are two reasons to use **POE**?

  _____

  _____

- I have accomplished _____ of the _____ goals stated in the Introduction chapter.

PLUGGING IN

"Algebraic symbols are used when you do not know
what you are talking about."

–Philippe Schnoebelen

READING

WRITING AND LANGUAGE

MATH

ESSAY

Goals Review

At the conclusion of this chapter, you will be able to accomplish the following:

- Understand *when* to Plug In or PITA
- Understand *how* to Plug In or PITA
- Understand *why* Plugging In and PITA are such powerful techniques

PLUGGING IN

ETS makes a big deal about the differences between Heart of Algebra questions and Passport to Advanced Math questions. However, those differences don't matter too much to us. If there are variables in a question, turn it into an arithmetic question by Plugging In numbers.

7. If $2b + b + \dfrac{1}{2}b = a$, what is the value of $b - a$, in terms of a ?

A) $-\dfrac{5}{2}a$

B) $-\dfrac{5}{7}a$

C) $\dfrac{5}{7}a$

D) $\dfrac{5}{2}a$

Difficulty: Easy

PLUGGING IN BASIC APPROACH

1. Identify the variable(s).

2. Plug in a number for the variable(s).

3. Work the steps of the problem.

4. Circle the Target Number.

5. Use POE until only one answer choice is left.

---

23. If the expression $\dfrac{6x^2}{3x - 6}$ is written in the equivalent form $\dfrac{24}{3x - 6} + N$, what is N, in terms of x ?

A) $2x - 4$

B) $2x - 2$

C) $2x + 2$

D) $2x + 4$

Difficulty: Hard
Don't plug in for the lonely variable – N. Plug in for x.

WHAT TO PLUG IN

What happens if $x = 2$ in that last problem? Why would it be a bad idea to plug in $b = 37$ for the first problem? Choose numbers that make the arithmetic as straightforward as possible.

Difficulty: Medium
What's a good number to plug in for b ?

8. If $\dfrac{b}{6} = \dfrac{x+1}{3}$, what is x, in terms of b ?

A) $\dfrac{3b-1}{6}$

B) $\dfrac{b-6}{2}$

C) $\dfrac{b-2}{2}$

D) $2b - 1$

Plugging In Tips

- Try **numbers that make the math as straightforward as possible**, especially when calculator use is not allowed. Numbers like 2, 3, 5, and 10 work great, and 100 is good for percent questions.

- As long as your numbers **fit the requirements of the problem**, your numbers will be good, viable numbers to use. Even a weird target number will probably only match one answer choice.

- **Avoid using 0 and 1** whenever possible.

- If the question is about a **relationship between numbers, plug in**! The question may contain variables, fractions, or the phrase "in terms of."

- **Check all four answer choices** if they have variables. If two work, plug in again!

Let's try one more that could be tricky with algebra, but is much more straight-forward with actual numbers.

 20. Which of the following represents the expression $18(9^x)$ rewritten in the form $F \times G^{(2x + 2)}$?

A) $2 \times 2^{2x + 2}$

B) $3 \times 2^{2x + 2}$

C) $2 \times 3^{2x + 2}$

D) $3 \times 3^{2x + 2}$

Difficulty: Medium

The previous questions all had variables in the answer choices—a good sign that Plugging In is an option. The technique can work in most questions involving the relationship between numbers. Be on the lookout for hidden plug-ins. Instead of trying to imagine how the numbers behave, plug in numbers, and see what happens.

9. In the equation $f^g = 81$, where f and g are positive integers, how many different values of f are possible?

A) Two

B) Three

C) Four

D) Five

Difficulty: Medium
Plug-and-Play!
If $g = 1$, what is f?
If $g = 2$, what is f?
What else will work?

Plugging In can also be a useful technique on geometry questions that involve variables or unknown quantities. Just make sure to follow the rules of geometry when plugging in for lengths or angles.

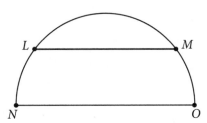

Difficulty: Medium

11. The semicircle above has a radius $r \geq 2$. If chord $\overline{LM}$ is parallel to diameter $\overline{NO}$, which of the following could be the length of $\overline{LM}$?

A) $\dfrac{3}{2}r$

B) r^2

C) $\dfrac{5}{2}r$

D) $\sqrt{5r}$

Plugging In can be a great tool for word problems too.

Difficulty: Medium
Are there variables?
Plug in!

17. The cost to ship a package with a certain shipping company is \$13 when the package weighs 20 pounds. With a weight of 30 pounds, the package costs \$17 to ship. If the cost increases at a constant rate as the weight of the package increases, which of the following linear models best describes the cost c in dollars to ship a package weighing p pounds?

A) $c = \dfrac{1}{4}p + 6.5$

B) $c = \dfrac{2}{5}p$

C) $c = \dfrac{2}{5}p + 5$

D) $c = \dfrac{5}{2}p + 5$

PLUGGING IN THE ANSWERS (PITA)

In the last problem, ETS gave you the numbers to Plug In within the question. Wouldn't it be nice if they always did that? It actually happens quite a bit! When the question asks for a specific amount and the answer choices are presented in numerical order, Plug In the Answers.

PITA BASIC APPROACH

1. Label the answer choices.

2. If the question asks for the greatest or smallest value, start there. Otherwise, start with one of the answers in the middle.

3. Work the steps, using Bite-Sized Pieces.

4. Eliminate answers that are too big or small.

5. When one of the answers works—STOP.

10. Which of the following is a possible solution to the equation

$$\frac{20}{a-1} - \frac{18}{a+1} = 2 ?$$

A) 4

B) 5

C) 6

D) 7

Difficulty: Medium

 16. If $8x^2 - 14x - 15 = 0$, then which of the following is the least value of x ?

A) $-\dfrac{5}{2}$

B) $-\dfrac{3}{4}$

C) $\dfrac{3}{4}$

D) $\dfrac{5}{2}$

Difficulty: Medium
Watch those parentheses when using your calculator!

Difficulty: Medium
Why can you eliminate
(A) immediately?

21. If $\dfrac{x^2 - 7x}{6} = 10$ and $x > 0$, what is the value of $x + 8$?

A) −5

B) 3

C) 13

D) 20

Plug In the Answers when:

- the question asks for a specific amount—"How much,"
  "How many," or "What is the value of…?"

- you are tempted to write your own equation

- there are numbers in the answer choices

PITA often works for word problems too!

Difficulty: Medium
When the question asks
for the greatest number
or the maximum value,
plug in that answer
choice first.

13. Nathan wants to give one noisemaker and one horn to each guest at his New Year's Eve party. If noisemakers cost 40 cents each and horns cost 35 cents each, and Nathan has only $20 to spend in total on noisemakers and horns, what is the maximum number of guests Nathan can have at his party?

A) 23

B) 24

C) 25

D) 26

Difficulty: Medium

18. A car begins at rest 200 meters from the finish line of a straight segment of track. If the car accelerates from rest at a constant rate of 4 meters per second each second, its distance from the finish line, x, is given by the equation $x = 200 - 2t^2$, where $0 \leq t \leq 10$. After how many seconds, t, has the car travelled 50 meters?

A) 2

B) 5

C) 9

D) 12

PLUGGING IN DRILL

Time: 10 minutes

Unless you are aiming for a top score, don't try all the questions! Use your POOD to choose the best ones for you.

5

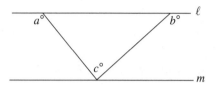

 E   In the figure above, if $\ell \parallel m$, what is the value of $a + b$ in terms of c ?

A) $360 - 2c$

B) $180 + 2c$

C) $180 + c$

D) $180 - c$

4

E   If the expression $n^2 - 2n - 8$ represents the net profit on the sale of n units of a product, which of the following values represents the number of units sold for which the net profit equals 0 dollars?

A)   2

B)   4

C)   6

D)   8

7

M   At a grain packaging company, sacks of grain are filled by a machine that weighs each sack to be sure that it holds between $24\frac{3}{4}$ and $25\frac{1}{4}$ pounds of grain. Only then will a sack be sealed and shipped. If a sack holding b pounds of grain is shipped, which of the following describes all possible values of b ?

A) $|b - 25| > \dfrac{1}{4}$

B) $|b + 25| = \dfrac{1}{4}$

C) $|b - 25| = \dfrac{1}{4}$

D) $|b - 25| < \dfrac{1}{4}$

12

 M   Meg purchased a new computer for $2,800 that depreciates in value by 5% every month that she owns it. Which of the following expressions, $f(m)$, represents how much the computer is valued after m months?

A) $f(m) = 2800 - 0.05m$

B) $f(m) = 2800 - 0.05^m$

C) $f(m) = 2800 \times (1 - 0.05)m$

D) $f(m) = 2800 \times (1 - 0.05)^m$

COURSE WORKBOOK FOR THE SAT & PSAT

15

 M If $\dfrac{3}{x} - 13 = 10x$, then x could equal which of

the following?

A) 0.2

B) 0.5

C) 0.6

D) 1.5

27

 H Which of the following is equivalent to

$\dfrac{51x^3 - 24x^2 + 27x - 21}{3x - 6}$?

A) $17x^2 - 42x + 93 - \dfrac{579}{3x - 6}$

B) $17x^2 - 42x + 75 + \dfrac{450}{3x - 6}$

C) $17x^2 + 26x + 61 + \dfrac{345}{3x - 6}$

D) $17x^2 + 26x - 43 - \dfrac{279}{3x - 6}$

14

H If g and q are positive integers, such that

$g = \left(\dfrac{6}{5}\right)x$ and $x = \dfrac{q^2}{4}$, what is the LEAST

possible value of q ?

A) 18

B) 24

C) 30

D) 36

162 | © TPR Education IP Holdings, LLC

Summary

- What are the **advantages** of **Plugging In**?

  _____

  _____

- What are some **clues** that you can **Plug In**?

  _____

  _____

  _____

  _____

- What are the **steps** for **Plugging In**?

  _____

  _____

  _____

  _____

  _____

- What are some **good numbers** to use when Plugging In to make the math more convenient?

  _____

- What are some **clues** that you can **PITA**?

  _____

  _____

  _____

  _____

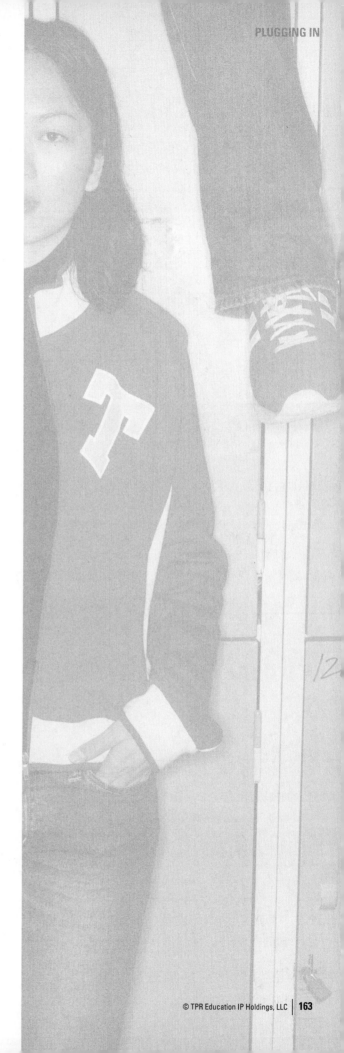

| **163**

- What are the **steps** for **PITA**?

  _____

  _____

  _____

  _____

- I have accomplished _____ of the _____ goals stated in the Introduction chapter.

FUNDAMENTALS

"The essence of mathematics is not to make simple things complicated,
but to make complicated things simple."

–Stan Gudder

Making It Up

You may have "that friend," the one who never studies for anything at all and still gets good grades, at least when the exam is an essay. She or he sounds really smart in the essay, even if she or he doesn't say anything of substance. What might be some drawbacks to this approach?

Goals Review

At the conclusion of this chapter, you will be able to accomplish the following:

- Understand *when* to solve for a variable or variables
- Understand *how* to solve for a variable or variables
- Understand *how* to solve simultaneous equations
- Understand *how* to translate word problems into math problems

Beyond Plugging In

Plugging In and Plugging In the Answers are great tools for a wide variety of questions, as seen in the last chapter. But what do you do when PITA isn't an option or Plugging In seems too complicated or time-consuming? Two other essential skills for the SAT Math sections include Solving and Translating. Let's see how they can help you score more.

SOLVING

Sometimes, ETS wants students to solve equations by manipulating them. If you can't use Plugging In or PITA and need to solve for a variable, you need to isolate that variable. Operations done to one side of the equation need to also be performed on the other side of the equation. You have probably done this a lot in Math class, so we will focus on some of the strange ways ETS might present solving questions.

1. Did you RTFQ? What are you solving for?
2. Can you use Plugging In or PITA?

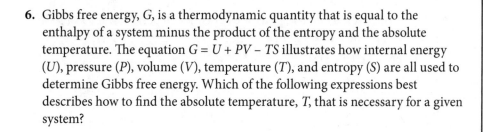

Isolate the variable. Do the same thing to both sides of the equation.

6. Gibbs free energy, G, is a thermodynamic quantity that is equal to the enthalpy of a system minus the product of the entropy and the absolute temperature. The equation $G = U + PV - TS$ illustrates how internal energy (U), pressure (P), volume (V), temperature (T), and entropy (S) are all used to determine Gibbs free energy. Which of the following expressions best describes how to find the absolute temperature, T, that is necessary for a given system?

A) $T = \dfrac{G - U + PV}{S}$

B) $T = \dfrac{G - U - PV}{S}$

C) $T = \dfrac{U - PV - G}{S}$

D) $T = \dfrac{U + PV - G}{S}$

Difficulty: Medium
Don't panic when you see all these variables and this long, long question! Just solve the equation for T.

Inequalities

Solving inequalities in one variable is a lot like solving equations. Whatever you do to one side of the inequality must also be done to the other side. The only difference, and it is an important one, is that you <u>must</u> flip the inequality sign when you multiply or divide by a negative number.

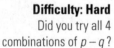

When solving an inequality, remember to flip the sign if you multiply or divide by a negative number.

Difficulty: Medium

8. If $13 \le 31 - 2x \le 39$, which of the following represents all possible values of x?

A) $-9 \le x \le 4$

B) $-4 \le x \le 9$

C) $9 \le x \le 22$

D) $22 \le x \le 35$

A more difficult inequality question may ask you to combine the ranges of two variables. Just remember to try all the possible combinations.

Difficulty: Hard
Did you try all 4 combinations of $p - q$?

23. Which of the following accurately defines all possible values of $p - q$ if $15 \le p \le 30$ and $7 \le q \le 19$?

A) $-4 \le (p - q) \le 23$

B) $-4 \le (p - q) \le 30$

C) $8 \le (p - q) \le 11$

D) $15 \le (p - q) \le 23$

Quadratics

Questions that ask for the specific factors, zeroes, solutions, or roots of quadratics can often be solved with Plugging In and PITA. Harder questions may ask about some mathematical operation such as the sum or product of those roots.

11. What is the sum of the distinct possible values of x for the equation $x^2 + 3x - 10 = 0$?

A) −3

B) −2

C) 3

D) 5

Difficulty: Medium

When a quadratic is in the form $ax^2 + bx + c = 0$:

The **sum** of the roots equals $-\dfrac{b}{a}$.

The **product** of the roots equals $\dfrac{c}{a}$.

If you need to multiply the factors of a quadratic, use FOIL.

Try to use Plugging In or PITA on quadratics. When a quadratic is difficult to factor, remember the quadratic formula:

$$x = \frac{-b \pm \sqrt{b^2 - 4ac}}{2a}$$

Rational Equations

8. If $\dfrac{2m}{5} = \dfrac{m+3}{12}$, what is the value of m ?

A) $\dfrac{3}{19}$

B) $\dfrac{1}{3}$

C) $\dfrac{15}{19}$

D) 5

Difficulty: Easy

Which is faster here—PITA or cross-multiplying and solving?

Solving on paper with a pencil can sometimes be faster and more accurate than using a calculator.

Another way ETS may present solving with fractions may look like the one below. To solve this one, first find a common denominator for the two fractions using the Bowtie Method.

Difficulty: Medium

18. If $\dfrac{3}{2x} - \dfrac{1}{4} = 2$, what is the value of x ?

Bowtie method

1. Multiply diagonally up (opposing denominators and numerators).

$$\overset{12}{\dfrac{3}{2x}} \times \overset{2x}{\dfrac{1}{4}}$$

2. Carry up the addition or subtraction sign.

$$\overset{12}{\dfrac{3}{2x}} \overset{-}{\times} \overset{2x}{\dfrac{1}{4}}$$

3. Add or subtract across the top.

$$\overset{12}{\dfrac{3}{2x}} \overset{-}{\times} \overset{2x}{\dfrac{1}{4}} = \dfrac{12 - 2x}{}$$

4. Multiply across the bottom.

$$\overset{12}{\dfrac{3}{2x}} \overset{-}{\times} \overset{2x}{\dfrac{1}{4}} = \dfrac{12 - 2x}{8x}$$

Now set that equal to 2, and solve for x !

READING

WRITING AND LANGUAGE

MATH

ESSAY

Exponents and Roots

Many questions about exponents and roots can be solved with Plugging In and PITA. When things get tricky to solve, it is sometimes best to plug in, and let your calculator do the hard work for you. However, sometimes that is not an option, as in the following question.

17. If $\sqrt{x^2 + 6x + 9} = 7$, what is the positive value of x?

Difficulty: Medium

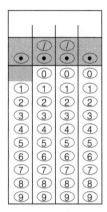

Sometimes, solving rational and roots questions makes the math do funny things. You may solve an equation and get answers that won't work when plugged back into the original equation. These are referred to as "extraneous solutions." The good news is that using PITA can be a great way to avoid these traps. Let's look at one on which PITA won't work and solving is necessary.

$$a - 3 = 2\sqrt{a}$$

10. Which of the following is the extraneous solution for a in the equation above?

A) 1

B) 2

C) 6

D) 9

Difficulty: Medium
Why can't you just use PITA?

Extraneous solutions don't work because they make a denominator of a rational expression equal to zero, lead to the calculation of a square root of a negative number, or give a negative value for a square root.

ETS also likes to test some weirder concepts about roots and exponents, like fractional or negative ones. Let's start with a question that only has one variable to deal with.

Difficulty: Easy

Remember **MADSPM**!
M _____
A _____
D _____
S _____
P _____
M _____

5. $\dfrac{\left(x^{\frac{1}{3}}\right)^2}{x^{\frac{1}{6}}} =$

A) $x^{\frac{1}{3}}$

B) $x^{\frac{1}{2}}$

C) $x^{\frac{2}{3}}$

D) $x^{\frac{13}{6}}$

With fractional exponents, the numerator is the exponent, and the denominator is the root. Think of it as "Power over Root." For negative exponents, calculate the positive exponent, then take the reciprocal.

Difficulty: Medium

9. Which of the following is NOT equivalent to $\dfrac{1}{a^2}$?

A) $\left(a^{-10}\right)\left(a^{-4}\right)^{-2}$

B) $\dfrac{a^{-4}}{a^{-2}}$

C) $\left(a^2\right)^{-1}$

D) $\left(\dfrac{1}{a^{-1}}\right)^2$

Two (or More) Variables

So far, we've mostly looked at equations and expressions with one variable. ETS will increase the difficulty of some questions by bringing in more variables or another equation. Don't panic, though! TPR strategies can make these situations more manageable.

22. If $x \neq 0$ and $y \neq 0$, which of the following expressions is equivalent to

$$\left(\frac{36x^3 y^2}{64x^7 y^4} \right)^{-\frac{1}{2}} ?$$

A) $\dfrac{3x^2 y}{4}$

B) $\dfrac{3}{4x^2 y}$

C) $\dfrac{4x^2 y}{3}$

D) $-\dfrac{3}{4x^2 y}$

For questions with weird exponents and roots, try to plug in, and remember MADSPM.

Difficulty: Medium

Don't forget about Bite-Sized Pieces! What happens when you calculate $\left(\dfrac{36}{64} \right)^{-\frac{1}{2}}$? How does knowing the answer help you use POE?

Difficulty: Medium

What happens when

you simplify $\sqrt[3]{\dfrac{x^2}{x^{-4}}}$?

How does knowing the

answer help with POE?

21. If $x \neq 0$ and $y \neq 0$, which of the following expressions is equivalent to

$$\sqrt[3]{\dfrac{x^2 y^{-3}}{x^{-4} y^6}} \ ?$$

A) $\dfrac{1}{\sqrt[3]{x^2}\,(y)}$

B) $\dfrac{x^3}{\sqrt{y^9}}$

C) $\dfrac{x^2}{y^3}$

D) $\dfrac{1}{3}\left(\dfrac{x^6}{y^9}\right)$

Besides seeing two variables in exponent questions, you may also come across a two-variable equation like the one below. There are no answer choices to PITA, so solve it!

Difficulty: Medium

How can you get rid of the fractions in the equation?

18. If $\dfrac{2}{3}a + \dfrac{3}{4}b = 14$, what is the value of $8a + 9b$?

Remember to RTFQ. Be sure of what the question asks, and find the most straightforward way to get there.

Simultaneous Equations

When given two equations with two variables, there are a number of approaches to take. Start by making sure to RTFQ—in some cases, you don't even need to solve for the variables. If you are very skilled with a graphing calculator, graphing the two equations and finding the point or points of intersection can be the most efficient way to solve the problem. If navigating a calculator would slow you down too much or if your calculator crashes on test day (yikes!), solving by elimination or substitution can be very efficient and effective as well. The way the equations are written will determine whether you use elimination or substitution to solve.

3. If $4x - 5y = 15$ and $2x - y = 9$, then $6x - 6y =$

A) 9

B) 15

C) 24

D) 30

Difficulty: Easy
Make sure to RTFQ!

15. If $2a + 3c - 5b = 7$ and $13b - a - 6c = 10$, which of the following is the value of $a + b$?

A) 7

B) 8

C) 9

D) 10

Difficulty: Medium
The final question doesn't ask about c, so try to make it disappear.

Stack the equations up, then add or subtract. If you need to solve for one variable, try to make the other one disappear! Sometimes, you may need to manipulate one of the equations first.

$$2y = 1 - 3x$$
$$-5 - x = 2y$$

19. Based on the system of equations above, what is the value of $x - y$?

A) −4

B) −1

C) 3

D) 7

Difficulty: Medium
Is elimination still the best way to solve this system?

If the two equations in a system are already set equal to the same quantity, set them equal to each other and solve.

One final way ETS may test systems of equations is by asking for the number of solutions the system has. All the previous systems only had one solution, but sometimes two lines have no solutions (because they are parallel) or infinitely many solutions (because they are exactly the same line).

$$\frac{y-3}{2} = x$$

$$ax - 2y = -6$$

Difficulty: Medium

7. If the system of equations above has infinitely many solutions, what is the value of a ?

A) -4

B) -2

C) 2

D) 4

When dealing with linear equations, a system with infinitely many solutions means the two equations represent the same line. A system with no solutions means the lines are parallel. In either case, both lines have the same slope.

$$\frac{1}{3}x - \frac{5}{6}y = 4$$

$$rx - 10y = 24$$

Difficulty: Medium

When a line is in the standard form $Ax + By = C$, the slope $= -\dfrac{A}{B}$ and y-intercept $= \dfrac{C}{B}$.

10. Consider the linear system of equations above, in which r is a constant. If the system has no solution, what is the value of r ?

A) 8

B) 4

C) $\dfrac{5}{2}$

D) $\dfrac{2}{5}$

TRANSLATING ENGLISH TO MATH

Sometimes, the question doesn't even give an equation, just a description of the situation. Translate the words in the question into an equation, using Bite-Sized Pieces.

4. Aimee's mobile phone service allows her phone to serve as a Wi-Fi hotspot. The service charges a flat monthly fee of $4 plus 3 cents per gigabyte (GB) of data usage. Aimee wants to spend less than $15 on the hotspot service this month. If g represents the number of GB of data usage, which of the following inequalities correctly describes the situation?

A) $0.03g < 15$

B) $4 + 0.03g < 15$

C) $4 + 3g < 15$

D) $g(4 + 0.03) < 15$

Difficulty: Easy
Remember to use POE after each Bite-Sized Piece!

English	Math Equivalents
% (percent)	
of	
what	
is, are, were, did, does	
out of	
per	
less than	
less than or equal to	
greater than	
greater than or equal to	
at least	
no more than	

Sometimes ETS asks for the system of equations that could be solved to find a quantity in a given situation. Translate the most straightforward piece of information first, and use POE.

Difficulty: Medium

What piece of information makes the most sense to you? Start there!

12. A used bookstore sells paperback books for $3.50 and hardback books for $5.25. Karina made three visits to the bookstore, and in total over the three visits, Karina bought 13 books for a total cost of $56. Solving which of the following systems of equations yields the number of paperback books, *x*, and the number of hardback books, *y*, that Karina bought at the used bookstore over the three visits?

A) $x + y = 56$
   $3.5x + 5.25y = 13$

B) $x + y = 13$
   $3.5x + 5.25y = 56 \times 3$

C) $x + y = 13$
   $3.5x + 5.25y = \dfrac{56}{3}$

D) $x + y = 13$
   $3.5x + 5.25y = 56$

On a hard translation question, start with the most straightforward piece of information, and use Bite-Sized Pieces.

Difficulty: Medium

What do you need to solve this question?

18. Kristine needs to purchase both T-shirts and pairs of shorts for a vacation she is taking to Hawaii. After contacting the local clothing store, she knows that five T-shirts and three pairs of shorts will cost her $30.50 and that two T-shirts and six pairs of shorts will cost her $41.00. Based on this information, what is the cost of the seven T-shirts and nine pairs of shorts that Kristine will need for her trip, if all shirts cost the same price and all shorts cost the same price?

A) $8.50

B) $17.50

C) $59.50

D) $71.50

Term	Definition	Examples
Number		
Integer		
Negative		
Positive		
Even		
Odd		
Difference		
Sum		
Product		
Quotient		
Ratio		
Prime		
Factor/Divisor		
Prime factor		
Multiple		
Remainder		
Distinct		
Consecutive		
Absolute Value		
The square of...		
The square root of...		
Mean		
Median		
Mode		
Percent		
Inclusive		
Range		
Reciprocal		
Rational		
Radical		
Extraneous Solution		
Linear Equation		
Quadratic Equation		
Quadratic Formula		

FUNDAMENTALS DRILL

Time: 10 minutes

Unless you are aiming for a top score, don't try all the questions! Use your POOD to choose the best ones for you.

4

E If $\dfrac{x}{y} - 4 = 2 + \dfrac{1}{y}$, then which of the

following is equivalent to x, in terms of y ?

A) $x = y + 6$

B) $x = \dfrac{6}{y}$

C) $x = 6y + 1$

D) $x = y - \dfrac{1}{6}$

5

$$\frac{-5}{3x + 2} = \frac{2}{4 - 5x}$$

E In the equation above, what is the value of x ?

A) $-\dfrac{24}{19}$

B) $-\dfrac{16}{19}$

C) $\dfrac{16}{31}$

D) $\dfrac{24}{19}$

11

M During a sale at an electronics store, all video games normally priced at $50 are 30% off, and all DVDs normally priced at $20 are 25% off. Marcela has up to $200 to spend on video games and DVDs during the sale, and she wants the number of DVDs she buys to be at least twice the number of games she buys. If a tax of 8% is applied to her total purchase, which of the following systems of inequalities can be solved for the number of video games, g, and the number of DVDs, d, that Marcela can buy?

A) $0.92(37.5g + 14d) \le 200$
$$d \ge 2g$$

B) $1.08(35g + 15d) \le 200$
$$d \ge 2g$$

C) $1.08(35g + 15d) \ge 200$
$$2g \ge d$$

D) $35g + 15d \le (1.08)(200)$
$$d \le 2g$$

13

 M If $\sqrt{x^2 - 6x - 66} = 5$, then what are the roots of the equation?

A) $x = -7;\, x = 13$

B) $x = 7;\, x = -13$

C) $x = -7;\, x = -13$

D) $x = 7;\, x = 13$

20

 M   Which of the following expressions is equivalent to $\left(\dfrac{64x^9 y^{27}}{27z^3}\right)^{\frac{1}{3}}$?

A) $\dfrac{4x^3 y^9}{3z}$

B) $\dfrac{4x^3 y^9}{27z^3}$

C) $\dfrac{64x^3 y^9}{27z}$

D) $\dfrac{192x^9 y^{27}}{81z^3}$

19

H   If m percent of 50 is equal to 20 percent of n, then what is the value of $\dfrac{m}{n}$?

35

H   Company G charges its customers a flat fee of 5 dollars to stream their first 8 movies per month and 75 cents for each additional movie streamed within the same one-month period. Company H charges its customers a flat fee of 7 dollars to stream their first 10 movies per month and 60 cents for each additional movie streamed within the same one-month period. What is the maximum number of movies a customer could stream in a one-month period and save money using Company G instead of Company H?

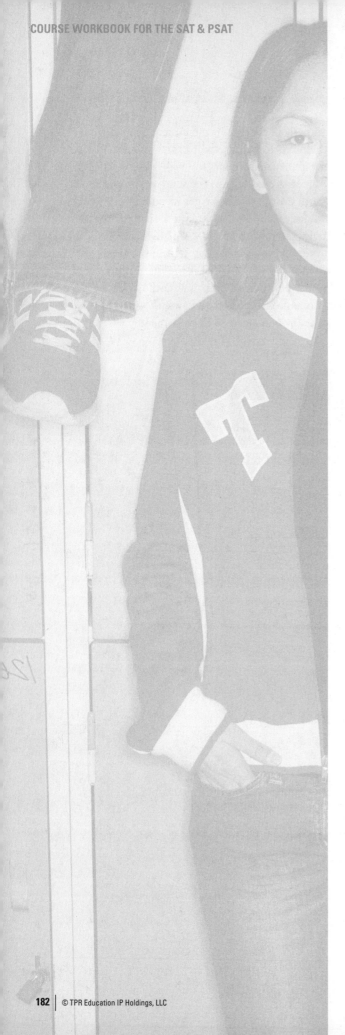

Summary

- What are two **essential math strategies** you can use when Plugging In and PITA are not effective options?

  _____

  _____

- What is the ultimate goal when **solving for a variable**?

  _____

- When **solving an inequality**, what must you remember to do when you multiply or divide by a negative number?

  _____

- When do you use the **Bowtie Method**?

  _____

- What is the standard form of a **quadratic equation**?

  _____

- When multiplying binomials, remember to use **FOIL**.

  F_____

  O_____

  I_____

  L_____

- When solving an equation, what situations could lead to **extraneous solutions**?

  _____

  _____

  _____

- What are the basic rules for **manipulating exponents**?

  M_____

  A _____

  D_____

  S _____

  P _____

  M_____

- What do the numerator and denominator represent in **fractional exponents**?

  _____

- What do you do to manipulate **negative exponents**?

  _____

- What are two ways to solve **simultaneous equations** without using a calculator?

  _____

  _____

- I have accomplished _____ of the _____ goals stated in the Introduction chapter.

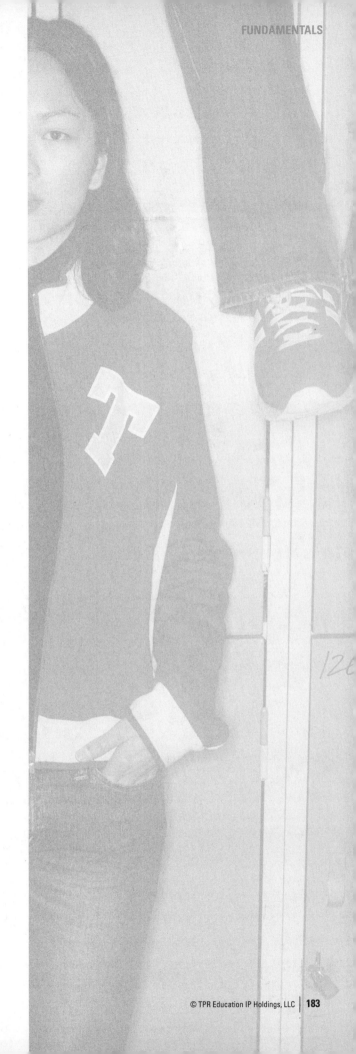

CHARTS
AND DATA

"It is a capital mistake to theorize before one has data."

—Sir Arthur Conan Doyle

Giving Presentations

You may have had to give a presentation in class before. Maybe you had a Physics lab where you had to present data to the class, or a History slideshow about some event. There is a lot of information, and it'd be boring to just read off a set of data. What were some ways you were able to present information that weren't just words?

Goals Review

At the conclusion of this chapter, you will be able to accomplish the following:

- Understand *how* to read figures, graphs, and tables
- Understand *how* to use graphics to find values and make predictions and inferences
- Understand *how* to draw a figure based on a description of a context
- Determine *whether* data collection methods and conclusions are appropriate

What's Up With All These Charts?

In an attempt to make the SAT a test that will better reflect what students learn in school and need to understand in the real world, ETS uses Charts and Tables to present data for students to analyze. The situations will typically include real-life applications, such as finance and business situations, social science issues, and scientific matter. Graphics will even show up in some Reading and Writing questions! This chapter will focus on how to read these graphics and do the statistical analysis ETS requires. **All of these questions will fall in the section in which calculator use is allowed, so use your calculator wisely.**

HOW TO READ A SCATTERPLOT GRAPH

Graphs can present data in a variety of ways. In the scatterplot graph on the following page, each dot represents one data point. Sometimes, a line or curve "of best fit" will be drawn to represent the equation that most closely matches the data. The term scatterplot isn't important, but the text on the graph is very important. Read the titles of all graphs, look for a key if there is one, and notice the units before answering any questions.

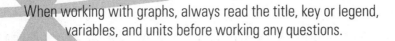

When working with graphs, always read the title, key or legend, variables, and units before working any questions.

Questions 10 and 11 refer to the following information.

The scatterplot below shows the income data for 24 selected part-time employees at Coffee Planet during a one-week period in March of 2014.

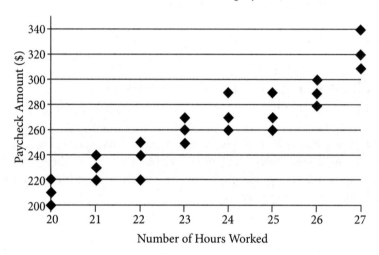

Income Data for Selected Part-Time Employees at Coffee Planet

Difficulty: Easy

Look It Up!

10. According to the scatterplot above, which of the following is closest to the average paycheck amount for the three part-time employees who worked 26 hours during the one-week period in question?

A) $280

B) $290

C) $300

D) $310

For Look It Up questions, read the graph or chart carefully, and use the scantron as a ruler if necessary. Don't give away points with careless errors.

11. If the trend in the relationship between the number of hours worked and paycheck amount remains consistent with the data above for part-time employees who worked more than 27 hours during the week in question, then which of the following would most likely be the paycheck amount earned by an employee who worked 28 hours during that week?

A) $290

B) $300

C) $330

D) $380

Difficulty: Medium
Find the Trend!

▲

For Find the Trend questions, continue the line of best fit off the edge of the graph, and see what the value would be at the given point.

Those last two questions were straightforward Look It Up questions. Sometimes, the questions will require "inferences" to be made. Don't worry, just look up the numbers to which each answer refers, and use POE!

READING

WRITING AND LANGUAGE

MATH

ESSAY

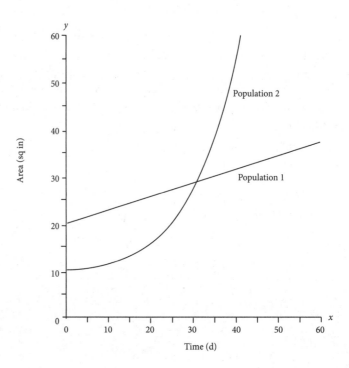

Difficulty: Medium

13. A scientist has two groups of mice in two wire cages that each have a base area of 60 square inches. After the initial groups of mice are added to each wire cage on Day 0, the researcher observes and records the area of the base of the cage covered by the total mice every 10 days. The results for each cage were modeled with the line or curve of best fit in the graph shown above, which relates the area of the base of the wire cage covered by mice as a function of time, in days. Which of the following inferences is NOT supported by the graph?

A) At Day = 0, Population 1 covered approximately 100% more of the area of the base of the cage than Population 2.

B) At Day = 30, Population 1 and 2 both covered the same area of the bases of their respective cages.

C) At Day = 60, the mice of both Population 1 and Population 2 covered less than 50% of the area of the base of their respective cages.

D) Population 1 models linear growth, while Population 2 models exponential growth.

HOW TO READ A BAR GRAPH

A bar graph is another way to represent data. Rather than giving points, each value for the variable at the bottom of the graph is represented by a bar. The height of the bar corresponds to a value on the left side of the graph. As always, read carefully, watch the units, and use POE!

When working with bar graphs, always read the title, key or legend, variables, and units before working any questions. Don't forget to use POE on the answer choices!

Bar graph or Histogram?
If the bars in a graph represent ranges of data, rather than distinct categories, ETS may use the term "histogram" to describe the figure. Just know that the same skills are used to answer the questions, no matter what the graph is called.

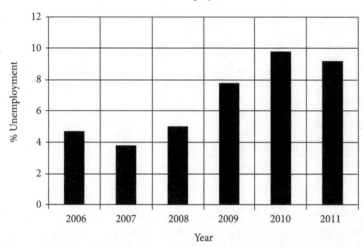

United States Unemployment Rate

8. The graph above shows the approximate national unemployment rate in the United States from 2006 to 2011. Based on the data presented in the graph, each of the following inferences would be justified EXCEPT:

A) The unemployment rate in 2010 was higher than that of any other year listed.

B) For each of the years listed, the unemployment rate increased.

C) The period from 2010 to 2011 experienced the highest unemployment rate of any two-year period listed.

D) The unemployment rate in 2007 was lower than that of any other year listed.

Difficulty: Easy
The word "except" in the question means to use POE to eliminate answers that are true.

Remember to RTFQ. Little words like "except" and "not" are really important!

HOW TO READ A TWO-WAY TABLE

Two-way tables give counts for data according to two variables. Much as how the previous graphics had one variable along the *x*-axis and one along the *y*-axis, two-way tables have categories listed across the top and down the left side of the table. Again, before answering any questions, read the headings, and note the units.

When working with two-way tables, always read the title, key or legend, variables, and units before working any questions. Don't forget to use POE on the answer choices!

Preferred Beverage by Gender

	Coffee	Tea	Hot Chocolate	Total
Men	923	254	89	1,266
Women	655	362	193	1,210
Total	1,578	616	282	2,476

Difficulty: Easy
Look up the numbers
for each answer choice
and use POE.

7. The student union at a local college sent a survey to all the members of the sophomore class in order to learn more about students' preferences regarding hot drinks. The students were asked to choose their top choice among three different beverage options: coffee, tea, and hot chocolate. The respondents' answers were counted and are shown in the two-way table above. Which of the following conclusions is best supported by the information in the table?

A) The number of women who prefer coffee is greater than the total number of people who prefer tea.

B) The number of men who prefer hot chocolate is greater than the number of women who prefer hot chocolate.

C) The number of men who prefer tea is greater than the total number of people who prefer hot chocolate.

D) The number of women who prefer tea or hot chocolate is greater than the number of women who prefer coffee.

Now let's move past the Look It Up questions on two-way tables to an Inference question. Just as with inference questions about charts, look up the numbers to which each answer refers and use POE!

Average Temperature in Degrees Fahrenheit by Month in Four Cities

City	May	June	July	August	September
Cairo	77	81	82	83	79
Istanbul	61	71	71	74	69
Stockholm	52	61	64	63	54
Tokyo	64	70	77	79	73

12. The average monthly temperatures, in degrees Fahrenheit, over a five-month period for four select cities are shown in the table above. A travel agent has advised a client that the warmest month in all four cities—Cairo, Istanbul, Stockholm, and Tokyo—is August. Based on the information in the table, is the travel agent's assessment accurate?

A) Yes, because the highest temperature listed for each of the four cities is in August.

B) Yes, because the lowest temperature listed for each of the four cities is July.

C) No, because the temperature listed for one of the cities is highest in July.

D) No, because the temperature listed for one of the cities is lowest in August.

Difficulty: Medium
If an answer includes a statement that isn't true, eliminate it!

TRANSLATING FIGURES

Remember Translating from the Fundamentals chapter? That skill also comes into play on some data questions that ask for the graph that best fits a given situation. Just translate the English in Bite-Sized Pieces, and use Process of Elimination on the answers at each step.

Difficulty: Medium
Right after school, how far is Everett from his house? What answers can be eliminated at that point?

15. Everett lives ten miles from school. He was driving home after class on a typical weekday afternoon when he suddenly realized that he had forgotten his calculator in his locker. He decided to return back to school and spent some time there talking to his Pre-Calculus teacher, whom he met in the hallway. After about twenty minutes at school, Everett got back into his car and drove straight home. Which of the following graphs best represents Everett's afterschool activity?

A)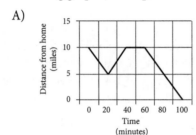

B)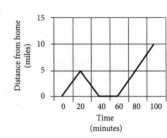

C)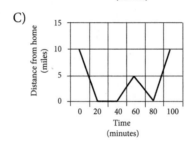

D)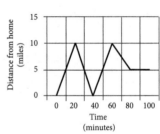

DATA COLLECTION METHODS

Occasionally, ETS will describe how a study was completed or an experiment was conducted and then require conclusions to be drawn from the description. These will appear as long, clunky word problems. Read very carefully, underlining key words in the question, and use Process of Elimination. Once you determine the variables being tested, try to determine whether the conclusion that is made can be directly drawn from the experimental or study design.

Use your pencil to underline key words and determine the variables being tested. Think about what would make for a good study with reasonable conclusions. Typically, the larger the number of unbiased individuals, the more accurate the results.

19. A candy company decided to conduct some product testing at a local college to determine whether there was a market for their new line of gummy bears. The market representatives set up a couple of tables inside the entrance to the college's student union building and handed out free samples of the gummy bears to passing students. Some of the students took the free samples, while others did not. Those who did take the free samples were asked to answer a brief survey about their opinion of the gummy bears. 70% of students who answered the survey stated that they would probably purchase the gummy bears should the company decide to market them on campus. Based on the survey results and the method of data collection described above, would the candy company executives be justified in claiming that a majority of students at this particular college would likely purchase the new line of gummy bears?

A) Yes, because the majority of students who answered the survey indicated that they would probably purchase the gummy bears.

B) Yes, because the fact that 70% of students who stated that they would probably purchase the gummy bears came from a non-representative sample means that the data collection methodology was flawed.

C) No, because the fact that 70% of students who stated that they would probably purchase the gummy bears came from a non-representative sample means that the data collection methodology was flawed.

D) No, because the majority of students who answered the survey indicated that they would probably not purchase the gummy bears.

Difficulty: Medium
That's a lot of words! What does your POOD tell you to do with this question?

On questions about justifying conclusions, eliminate answers that aren't supported by the data. Be careful not to make assumptions or extend the conclusion too far. Then use POE to get rid of answers that don't make sense to you, or just guess and go!

Difficulty: Medium

17. Ryan is curious to know whether there is a connection between video gaming and reading for his fellow high school students in the town of Port Harbor, Washington. He polls a random group of 100 high school students from Port Harbor and finds definitive proof of an inverse relationship between time spent video gaming and time spent reading. Which of the following statements is best supported by the data?

A) Using video gaming and reading as defined by Ryan's poll, a decrease in reading is caused by an increase in video gaming for high school students in the state of Washington.

B) Using video gaming and reading as defined by Ryan's poll, a decrease in reading is caused by an increase in video gaming for high school students in the town of Port Harbor.

C) There is an inverse relationship between time spent video gaming and time spent reading for high school students in the state of Washington.

D) There is an inverse relationship between time spent video gaming and time spent reading for high school students in Port Harbor.

CONFIDENCE INTERVALS AND MARGINS OF ERROR

When surveys are used to collect data, researchers want to make sure that they use a sample population that is representative of the general population to extrapolate their results. Two measures are used to determine this—confidence intervals and margins of error. For example, if a survey with a confidence level of 95% and a margin of error of ±3 were repeated 100 times, the results should be within 3 percentage points of the sample results 95 of the 100 times.

Difficulty: Medium

20. A prominent statistical organization conducted a random survey of 1,500 high school students from around the United States. The questionnaire asked students whether they like to listen to music while they do their homework. 570 students answered "yes" to this question. If the organization determines that its random survey results have a margin of error of 3%, which of the following best represents the approximate range for the percentage of students nationwide who likely enjoy listening to music while they do their homework?

A) 32–35%

B) 35–41%

C) 41–47%

D) 47–53%

CHARTS AND DATA DRILL
Time: 10 minutes

Unless you are aiming for a top score, don't try all the questions! Use your POOD to choose the best ones for you.
Note: Calculator permitted on all questions.

3

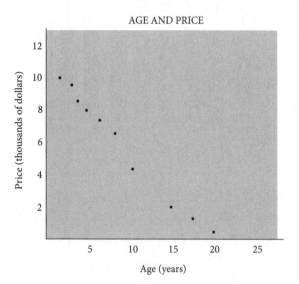

AGE AND PRICE

E The graph above shows the price and age for each of 10 cars of a certain model made by the Drive-o-Matic company. Which of the following is the best approximation for the price of a car that is 12 years old?

A) $2,100

B) $3,400

C) $5,200

D) $5,500

32

HANDEDNESS AMONG SEVENTH-GRADE BOYS AND GIRLS

	Boys	Girls
Left-handed	23	19
Right-handed	169	192
Total	192	211

E The table above shows the number of seventh graders who are left-handed or right-handed by gender in a certain middle school. What percent of all seventh graders in this school, rounded to the nearest percent, are right-handed boys? (Disregard the percent sign when gridding your answer.)

READING

WRITING AND LANGUAGE

MATH

ESSAY

14

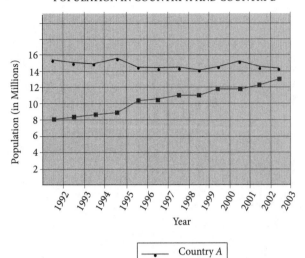

POPULATION IN COUNTRY *A* AND COUNTRY *B*

Country *A*
Country *B*

M   According to the data in the graph above, approximately how many more people lived in Country A than lived in Country B in 1998 ?

A)   3,200

B)   14,200

C)   3,200,000

D)   14,200,000

18

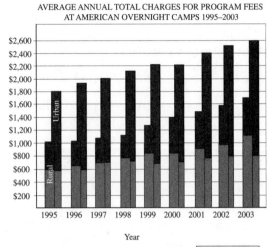

AVERAGE ANNUAL TOTAL CHARGES FOR PROGRAM FEES AT AMERICAN OVERNIGHT CAMPS 1995–2003

Room & Board
Program Fee

M   The graph above shows the financial data for American overnight camps from 1995-2003. For the program year in which charges for room and board at rural camps was most nearly equal to $1,100, what was the approximate charge for the program fee at urban camps?

A) $980

B) $1,025

C) $1,800

D) $2,600

21

ROUND-TRIP AIRFARE COSTS FROM NEW YORK

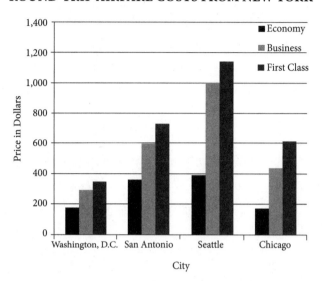

M   The bar graph above shows the round-trip airfare costs from New York City to four other cities in the United States. Which of the following is the closest approximation of the average cost for a business class ticket to each of these four cities?

A) $580

B) $645

C) $715

D) $920

24

ENROLLMENT LAST YEAR AT GROVETON HIGH SCHOOL

Class	Total Number of Students in Class	Number of Students Who Passed Chemistry
Junior	80	42
Senior	70	30

H   All of the students who took chemistry at Groveton High School last year were juniors or seniors, as shown in the table above. If 80% of the students who took chemistry passed, then what fraction of the students in the combined junior and senior classes took chemistry?

A) $\frac{48}{125}$

B) $\frac{12}{25}$

C) $\frac{1}{2}$

D) $\frac{3}{5}$

27

H In a poll conducted several weeks before a local election for town sheriff, 49% of respondents stated that they intended to vote for Candidate A, while 51% of respondents stated that they intended to vote for Candidate B. Since the sample size of this poll was 1,200 town residents, the margin of error was estimated to be ± 3. If Candidate A actually won the election with 51% of all votes cast, then which of the following conclusions is most supported by the data?

A) The poll numbers accurately predicted the outcome of the election.

B) The poll numbers were too close to make an accurate prediction about the outcome of the election.

C) The poll numbers incorrectly predicted the outcome of the election.

D) No conclusions can be made using the poll numbers.

Summary

- When **working with any type of graphic,** what four items should you always look at before working through the questions?

  _____

  _____

  _____

  _____

- What is the best way to deal with **"Look It Up"** questions that ask for a data point shown on the graph?

  _____

- What is the best way to deal with **"Find the Trend"** questions that ask for a data point not shown on the graph?

  _____

- What is the best way to deal with **"Inference"** questions about charts and figures?

  _____

- What factors are important to think about when a question asks about the **validity of data collection methods and samples**?

  _____

- What are two measures researchers use to describe the **accuracy of survey data**?

  _____

  _____

- I have accomplished _____ of the _____ goals stated in the Introduction chapter.

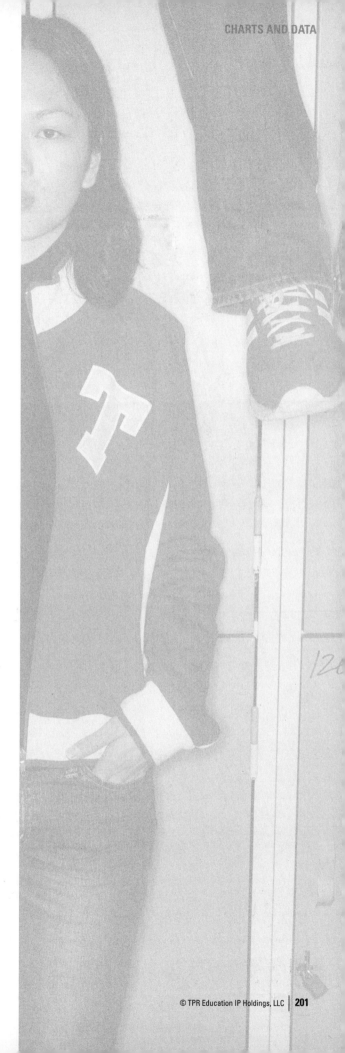

ARITHMETIC

"If a hen and a half can lay an egg and a half in a day and a half,
how long does it take a monkey with a wooden leg
to kick the seeds out of a dill pickle?"

—Tom Robbins

READING

WRITING AND LANGUAGE

MATH

ESSAY

Numbers = Facts?

You may have heard the old joke "87% of statistics are made up." Yet, there are numbers all around you. The probability of rain tomorrow, the number of points your favorite sports team scored last night, the number of Twitter followers you have, even your SAT score and GPA are numbers that affect your life. What sort of things do numbers mean, and what do they NOT tell you about a situation?

Goals Review

At the conclusion of this chapter, you will be able to accomplish the following:

- Understand *how* to stay organized to solve Data Analysis questions
- Understand *how* to stay organized to solve Problem-Solving questions
- Understand *when* and *how* to tackle Extended Thinking questions

DATA ANALYSIS

Several questions on the SAT will ask for information about a set of numbers, either from a table or graphic or in the context of a word problem. This section will deal with the tools to keep you organized on the Data Analysis questions. **Calculators will be allowed on all of the questions in this chapter.**

Mean = Average

SAT questions that ask for the average or mean of a set of numbers can often contain tricky language or a lot of information. Take the question in Bite-Sized Pieces, and use an Average Pie to organize the numbers.

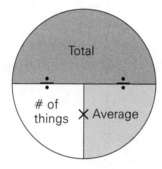

14. At a certain chess competition, the mean years of experience of all expert players is 14 years, and the mean years of experience of all novice players is 6 years. Which of the following must be true about the mean years of experience, x, of all chess players, both expert and novice, at the competition?

A) $x = 10$

B) $x > 10$

C) $x < 10$

D) $6 < x < 14$

See the word "average" or "mean"? Draw a pie. See a variable? Plug in!

Median = Middle

The median is the middle number of an ordered group of numbers. If there are an even number of elements in the set, the median is the average of the two numbers in the middle.

Average Temperature in Degrees Fahrenheit by Month in Four Cities

City	May	June	July	August	September
Cairo	77	81	82	83	79
Istanbul	61	71	71	74	69
Stockholm	52	61	64	63	54
Tokyo	64	70	77	79	73

Which numbers do you need from the chart? What do you do with them?

11. The average monthly temperatures, in degrees Fahrenheit, over a five-month period for four select cities are shown in the table above. According to the data in the table, the median of the monthly average temperatures from May to September in Stockholm is how much less than the median of the monthly average temperatures from May to September in Cairo?

A) 6°F

B) 10°F

C) 12°F

D) 20°F

Mode = Most

The mode is the number that appears the most often in a group of numbers.

▼

Questions 21 and 22 refer to the following information.

The scores on the 100-point midterm exam recently taken by the 10 students enrolled in AP Art History at Yorktown High School are shown in list A below. The scores on the 100-point midterm exam recently taken by the 12 students enrolled in AP Psychology are shown in list B below.

A: {61, 64, 75, 75, 78, 83, 86, 88, 92, 96}
B: {65, 71, 71, 71, 74, 74, 81, 83, 85, 88, 94, 95}

 21. Which of the following conclusions is best supported by the data provided above?

    A) The mode of midterm exam scores in AP Art History was lower than the mode of midterm exam scores in AP Psychology.

    B) The mean of midterm exam scores in AP Art History was equal to the mean of midterm exam scores in AP Psychology.

    C) The mean of midterm exam scores in AP Art History was lower than the mean of midterm exam scores in AP Psychology.

    D) The mean of midterm exam scores in AP Art History was higher than the mean of midterm exam scores in AP Psychology.

Look It Up!

Range = Greatest – Least

Range is the positive difference between the greatest number on the list and the least number on the list. Another way to think of it is the distance between these two numbers on a number line.

 22. According to the data provided, the range of student scores on the midterm exam in AP Art History at Yorktown High School was how many points greater than the range of student scores on the midterm exam in AP Psychology?

    A) 0

    B) 2

    C) 3

    D) 5

Look It Up!

▲

Standard Deviation

Standard Deviation is a measure of the spread of the numbers on a list or how much some of the numbers deviate from the average. If the numbers are close together, there is a small Standard Deviation, and if the numbers are far apart, there is a large Standard Deviation. ETS does not expect students to calculate Standard Deviation, but knowing the term is important.

Use POE!

4. Which of the following lists of numbers has the smallest standard deviation?

    A) {1, 3, 4, 5, 7}

    B) {14, 15, 15, 15, 16}

    C) {10, 20, 30, 40, 100}

    D) {−100, 0, 5, 200}

PROBLEM-SOLVING

The other part of the Problem Solving and Data Analysis sub-score comes from answering questions about such things as probability, rates, and proportions. Again, attacking the questions in Bite-Sized Pieces and keeping the information organized are the keys to success. Calculator use is allowed on these as well, so use it wisely!

Probability

Probability is the likelihood that something will happen. It is always expressed as a fraction or a decimal between 0 and 1, inclusive. A probability of 0 means that the event will never happen, and a probability of 1 means that the event will definitely happen.

$$\text{Probability} = \frac{\text{\# of outcomes that fit the requirements}}{\text{total \# of possible outcomes}}$$

Preferred Beverage by Gender

	Coffee	Tea	Hot Chocolate	Total
Men	923	254	89	1,266
Women	655	362	193	1,210
Total	1,578	616	282	2,476

12. The student union at a local college sent a survey to all the members of the sophomore class in order to learn more about students' preferences regarding hot drinks. The students were asked to choose their top choice among three different beverage options: coffee, tea, and hot chocolate. The respondents' answers were counted and are shown in the two-way table above. According to the data in the table, if a sophomore from among these respondents were to be chosen at random, what is the probability that he is a man who does NOT prefer tea?

A) $\dfrac{506}{633}$

B) $\dfrac{127}{633}$

C) $\dfrac{127}{1,238}$

D) $\dfrac{253}{619}$

Which numbers do you need from the chart? What do you do with them?

Rates and Unit Conversion

Rate questions are similar to average questions—they may ask about the average speed, the distance traveled, or how long a job took. All rate questions involve dividing the amount of work done, or the distance, by time. Use a Rate Pie to organize the information on questions like these.

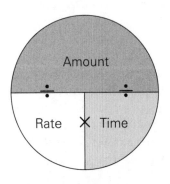 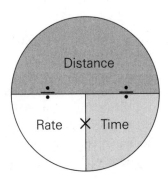

Make sure to use consistent units.

 13. Claudia's computer can download a 6-megabyte file in one second. If Claudia is shopping in an online music store and decides to purchase and download sixteen full-length music albums averaging 110 megabytes each, approximately how long, in <u>minutes</u>, would the download process take?

A)   1

B)   5

C)   50

D)   300

Solving rate questions can often be made more difficult when the question provides information in inconsistent units—seconds and minutes, feet and miles, and so on. Always check the units, just as with table and chart questions, and convert them when necessary.

 15. Annalee bicycles down a long, straight road at a constant rate of 22 feet per second. How long will it take Annalee to ride her bicycle for 30 miles at this rate?
(5,280 feet = 1 mile)

A)   0.5 hours

B)   1 hour

C)   1.5 hours

D)   2 hours

Proportions and Variation

Unit conversion relates to proportional relationships—there are 12 inches in every foot, 60 seconds in every minute. Other types of proportional relationships on the test may include converting measurements on a scale drawing to real-world measurements or finding the relationship between two quantities that vary directly or inversely.

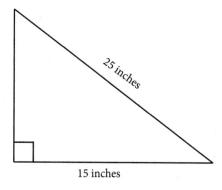

25 inches

15 inches

7. Jamie works as a stunt coordinator for famous motorcycle legend the Great Mazzini. She needs to construct a ramp for a jump the Great Mazzini will make over a number of empty school buses. She sketches out the triangular side of the ramp she will need on graph paper and uses the scale that 1 inch on the sketch will equal 2 yards on the actual ramp. What is the height of the ramp, in yards, that Jamie and her team will build?

A) 20

B) 40

C) 60

D) 80

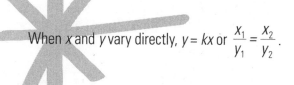

When x and y vary directly, $y = kx$ or $\dfrac{x_1}{y_1} = \dfrac{x_2}{y_2}$.

18. In 1976, Elvis consumed three times his body weight in peanut butter and banana sandwiches. If Elvis's body weight in 1976 was 250 pounds, and if a peanut butter and banana sandwich weighs four ounces, then how many such sandwiches did Elvis consume during 1976 ?
(1 pound = 16 ounces)

A) 1,000

B) 1,500

C) 3,000

D) 4,000

When x and y vary inversely, $y = \dfrac{k}{x}$ or $x_1 y_1 = x_2 y_2$.

32. The volume of hydrogen in a balloon varies inversely with the applied pressure. At an applied pressure of 200 torrs, the volume of hydrogen in the balloon is 3 cubic feet. What is the applied pressure, in torrs, when the volume of hydrogen in the balloon is 40 cubic feet?

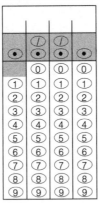

Ratios

Ratios are another way to show the relationship between two quantities. Ratios can be expressed in a variety of forms, such as "one cup of soda for every three cups of juice," "a ratio of 1 to 3," or mathematically as 1:3 or $\frac{1}{3}$. This last form, although it looks like a fraction, relates one part to another part, not the part to the whole.

▼

Questions 16 and 17 refer to the following information.

The movie-watching preferences of a randomly selected group of Americans aged 15–70 are represented in the table below. Survey participants were asked to choose their favorite genre of movie among the following categories: Action, Comedy, Drama, Romance, and Thriller.

Reported Favorite Movie Genre by Age Group

Age	Action	Comedy	Drama	Romance	Thriller
15–25	30,432	18,835	6,984	5,395	9,926
26–35	35,967	16,923	34,451	20,916	20,510
36–50	8,123	12,531	30,792	25,520	11,647
51–70	5,291	15,515	22,591	17,043	4,750

16. For marketing purposes, the surveyors wish to determine the relative preferences of Americans in different age brackets for each genre of movie in question. According to the data in the table above, the ratio of moviegoers who prefer Action to those who prefer Romance is greatest for which of the following age categories?

A) 15–25

B) 26–35

C) 36–50

D) 51–70

Which numbers do you need from the chart? What do you do with them?

Percents

Unlike ratios, percent questions do relate the part to the whole. Specifically, percent means "out of 100." Translating the English in the question into a mathematical expression is the key to solving percent questions.

English	Math Equivalents
% (percent)	
of	
what	
is, are, were, did, does	
out of	

What does your POOD tell you to do with this question?

17. Hearing about this survey before it was undertaken, an executive from a prominent Hollywood movie studio speculated that a minimum of 15% of moviegoers in all age categories would probably choose Drama as their favorite genre of movie. According to the data in the table, was the movie executive correct in her prediction?

A) Yes, because more than 15% of moviegoers in all age categories chose Drama.

B) Yes, because less than 15% of moviegoers in all age categories chose Drama.

C) No, because there is one age group for which less than 15% of moviegoers chose Drama.

D) No, because there are three age groups for which less than 15% of moviegoers chose Drama.

▲

Sometimes, a percent question will call for extrapolating from a sample in a study to the population at large. In this case, find the percent that fits the requirement in the sample, and take that percent of the larger population to see how many would fit the same requirement.

20. The Norwegian government recently conducted a poll among a randomly selected group of likely voters in order to determine the popularity of a certain proposal regarding national energy policy. Of the 2,000 people polled, 802 stated that they did not support the proposal in question. The government then conducted a follow-up poll among the likely voters who had stated that they do support the energy proposal. 567 of those who were polled a second time stated that they were very likely to vote for the policy in question, while the rest reported that they were somewhat likely to vote for the policy. Based on this data, approximately what percent of likely voters in Norway are somewhat likely to vote for the government's energy proposal?

A) 32%

B) 40%

C) 60%

D) 79%

Try Ballparking!

Percent Increase/Decrease

Percent change is a measure of how much something has increased or decreased relative to its original size. Use the formula below to calculate it. For percent increase, the smaller number is the original; for percent decrease, the larger number is the original.

$$\text{Percent Change} = \frac{\text{Difference}}{\text{Original}} \times 100$$

31. In the 1990s, the park rangers at Yellowstone National Park implemented a program aimed at increasing the dwindling coyote population in Montana. If there were 20 coyotes in the park in 1995 and 70 in 1997, by what percent did the coyote population increase in that time span? (Disregard the percent sign when gridding your answer.)

GROWTH AND DECAY

Another type of question related to changes in populations over time may ask about the growth or decay of a population or group. If something is increasing or decreasing by a constant percent or multiplier over a set period of time, use the growth/decay formula.

> The formula for exponential growth or decay is
>
> *final amount = original amount* $(1 \pm rate)^{number\ of\ changes}$
>
> when the growth is a **percent** of the total population or
>
> *final amount = original amount* $(multiplier)^{number\ of\ changes}$
>
> when the growth is a **multiple** of the total population

Knowing the formula will help you use POE. If calculator use were allowed, what other strategy could you use?

13. Ruwanthi paid $5,000 for her car when she bought it. Over the next several years, the car's value decreased by 10 percent per year. Which of the following functions gives the value, v, in dollars, of the car after n years at this rate?

A) $v(n) = 5,000 - 0.9n$

B) $v(n) = 5,000(0.9)^n$

C) $v(n) = 5,000(0.1)^n$

D) $v(n) = 5,000(1.1)^n$

SEQUENCES

Sequences are another way numbers increase or decrease in a set pattern.

In an **arithmetic** sequence, the *difference* between consecutive terms is constant. So keep adding or subtracting the same number to get the next term.

In a **geometric** sequence, the *ratio* between consecutive terms is constant. So keep multiplying or dividing by the same number to get the next term.

18. The following set represents the first four terms in a sequence: {16; 256; 4,096; 65,536}. Which of the following expressions does NOT correctly represent the terms in this sequence?

   A) 4^{2x}

   B) 8^x

   C) 2^{4x}

   D) 16^x

Look for ways to plug in on sequence questions.

EXTENDED THINKING

One fun trick ETS has decided to pull is the Extended Thinking question. It will appear as a pair of grid-ins based on the same information, and it can cover a wide variety of math concepts. The good news is that each question is scored separately, and one question is sometimes easier than the other. You might give that one a try. Unless you are shooting for a top score, though, the harder Extended Thinking questions are likely not in your POOD. Instead, spend your time on questions you have a better shot at getting right.

Which of these questions might be in your POOD?

Questions 37 and 38 refer to the following information.

Sheltingsby, GA, is a close-knit farming community with relatively little population growth, as many younger people depart each year to live in bigger cities. At the beginning of 2014, the population of Sheltingsby was 17,140, with 65% of all residents working in the agricultural industry. An additional 10% work in the next most popular industry, retail.

37. Based on the above information, at the beginning of 2014, what was the total number of Sheltingsby residents who do NOT work in either the agricultural or retail industries?

38. In an unexpected move, the government of Georgia announced that 1,000 acres of prime agricultural land will be released and made available for private purchase and use. Prior to this announcement, the expected current population of Sheltinsgby, y, could be modeled by the equation $y = 100x + 17,140$, where x is the number of years after 2014. Due to this announcement, however, the new expected current population can be modeled as $y = 375x^2 - 150x + 17,140$. In what year would the old population model have predicted as many residents as the new model is expected to have by 2020 ?

37.

38.

ARITHMETIC DRILL
Time: 10 minutes

Unless you are aiming for a top score, don't try all the questions! Use your POOD to choose the best ones for you.
Note: Calculator permitted on all questions.

▼

Questions 5 and 6 refer to the information below:

The table below shows the per capita income in U.S. dollars of four countries in select years, based on data from the World Bank.

Country	2007	2009	2011	2013
Afghanistan	$374	$451	$614	$665
Colombia	$4,664	$5,105	$7,125	$7,831
Denmark	$58,501	$57,896	$61,304	$59,382
Kenya	$847	$930	$998	$1,246

5

According to the data in the table above, the range of Kenya's per capita income from 2007 to 2013 was how much less than the range of Colombia's per capita income from the same time period?

A) $399

B) $2,768

C) $3,167

D) $6,585

6

The 2009 per capita income of a fifth country, New Zealand, was $27,562. If this data is combined with the data in the table, what was the average (arithmetic mean) per capita income of all five countries in 2009, rounded to the nearest whole dollar?

A) $18,389

B) $22,986

C) $64,382

D) $91,944

▲

Questions 10 and 11 refer to the following information:

The January sales figures for a certain electronics store are represented in the pie graph below.

Percentage of January Sales Revenue
(Total = $243,067)

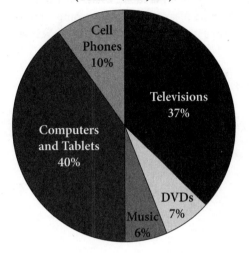

10

According to the data above, what was the approximate ratio of cell phone sales revenue to music sales revenue at the electronics store in January?

A) 10 : 7

B)   7 : 6

C)   5 : 3

D)   4 : 1

11

The revenue from the sales of DVDs was approximately what percent greater than the revenue from the sales of music at the electronics store in the month of January?

A)   1%

B)   13%

C)   14%

D)   17%

19

A scientist discovers that the number of a certain type of bacteria placed in a petri dish triples every hour. If the starting number of bacteria is 100, then how many bacteria can the scientist expect to find after 7 hours?

A)   2,700

B)   24,300

C)   72,900

D)   218,700

35

Lindsey and Stephen work at a factory. Lindsey can complete one full job in 3 hours, and Stephen can complete the same job in 5 hours. If Lindsey and Stephen work together on the job for 1 hour, then how long, in minutes, will it take Stephen to finish the job by himself?

36

The first three terms in a sequence are 13, 169, and 2,197. What is the units digit of the 7th term of the sequence?

Summary

- What are the definitions of **average**, **median**, and **mode**?

  _____

  _____

  _____

- What tool can you use to organize your information on **average** questions?

  _____

- What is the definition of **range**?

  _____

- What is the definition of **standard deviation**?

  _____

- What is the formula for **probability**?

  _____

- What tool can you use to organize your information on **rate** questions?

  _____

- What are the formulas for **direct** and **inverse** **variation**?

  _____

  _____

- What does a **ratio** represent?

  _____

- What is the formula for **percent change**?

  _____

- What are the two formulas for **exponential growth or decay**?

  _____

  _____

- In an **arithmetic sequence**, keep _____ to get the next term.

- In a **geometric sequence**, keep _____ to get the next term.

- I have accomplished _____ of the _____ goals stated in the Introduction chapter.

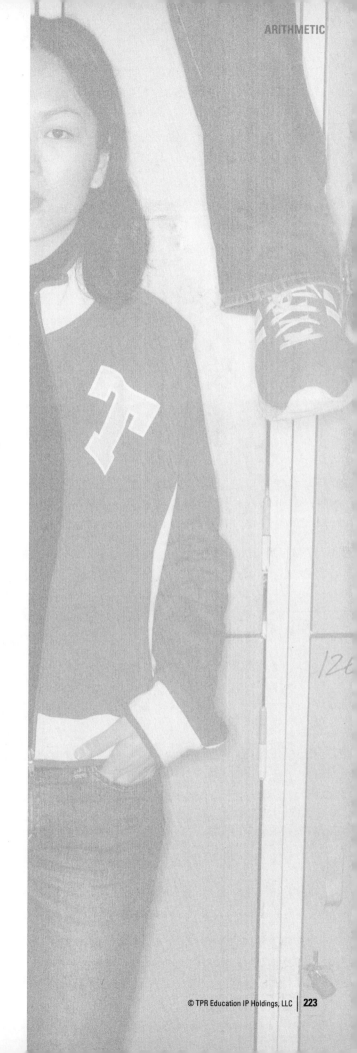

FUNCTIONS AND GRAPHS

"11:15 Restate my assumptions:
1. Mathematics is the language of nature.
2. Everything around us can be represented
and understood through numbers.
3. If you graph these numbers, patterns emerge.
Therefore: There are patterns everywhere in nature."

—Max Cohen in the film *Pi*

Rise of the Machines

Some of you may be fluent in technology. You're the person your family goes to when the computer starts acting up again. Others of you might be not so comfortable. You're happy when your phone is working, and it's time for a trip to the store when it's not. What are some ways we interact with computers and other sorts of machines in our everyday lives?

Goals Review

At the conclusion of this chapter, you will be able to accomplish the following:

- Understand *how* to interpret function notation
- Understand *how* to interpret graphs and their values and roots in the *xy*-plane
- Understand *how* to solve coordinate geometry questions in the *xy*-plane

FUNCTION BASICS

A function is a machine for producing ordered pairs. An x-value is put into the function, and the corresponding y-value comes out. This y-value is usually referred to as $f(x)$. The f in $f(x)$ is not a variable; it's just the name of the function.

1. If $f(x) = x^2 + 8x + 2$, then $f(3) =$
   A) 29
   B) 33
   C) 35
   D) 53

15. The function w is defined by $w(x) = 6 + 3x$. If $4 \cdot w(z) = 96$, what is the value of z?
    A)   3
    B)   6
    C) 10
    D) 78

The x goes in the function machine, and the y comes out, so $f(x) = y$.

ETS could also ask for the x-value that must be put into the function to get a certain y-value out.

12. If $f(x) = \left(\dfrac{1}{x}\right)^3$, what is one possible value of x for which

$$\frac{1}{216} < f(x) < \frac{1}{64}\ ?$$

   A) 3
   B) 4
   C) 5
   D) 6

What should you do when you see numbers in the answer choices?

FUNCTIONS IRL

Functions may show up in the form of wordy word problems as well. As always, read carefully, underline key words with your pencil, and take it in Bite-Sized Pieces. Look for ways to Ballpark, Plug In, or PITA.

3. Jack's band charges by the performance. Jack's share P, in dollars, for x performances is given by the function $P(x) = 1,200x - 60$. If Jack earned $4,740 one month playing with his band, how many performances did the band give?

A) 3

B) 4

C) 5

D) 6

14. Catherine is filling her swimming pool. The water is currently at a level of c inches, and the level of the water rises by i inches every r minutes. Which of the following functions represents the water level, in inches, after Catherine fills the pool for an additional m minutes?

A) $f(m) = c + m\left(\dfrac{i}{r}\right)$

B) $f(m) = c + m\left(\dfrac{r}{i}\right)$

C) $f(m) = c + i\left(\dfrac{r}{m}\right)$

D) $f(m) = c + imr$

For word problems containing functions, read carefully for key words, and look for ways to Plug In or PITA.

FUNCTIONS AND GRAPHS

Because functions yield ordered pairs in the *xy*-plane, many function questions will involve graphing. Let's start with the basics of points in the *xy*-plane.

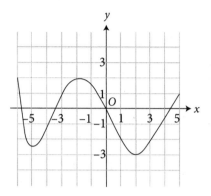

2. The figure above shows the graph of the function *f*. Which of the following is closest to *f*(–3) ?

A) –2

B) –1

C)   1

D)   2

If the question gives a number inside the *f*(*x*) parentheses, such as *f*(3), it means *x* = 3. From there, see what *y*-value intersects the line at *x* = 3.

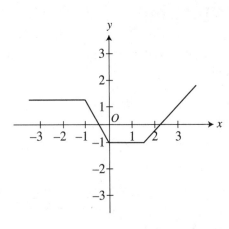

Remember: $y = f(x)$

4. The graph of $y = h(x)$ is shown above. If $h(x) = -1$, which of the following is a possible value of x ?

A) -2

B) -0.5

C) 0.5

D) 2

If the question gives a value for $f(x)$, such as $f(x) = 3$, it means $y = 3$.
From there, see what x-value intersects the line $y = 3$.

GET THE FUNC OUT

So far, we've looked at questions in which ETS described the situation or the graph and asked for some information about it. ETS will also provide the graph and ask questions about the equation it represents or specific values from the graph.

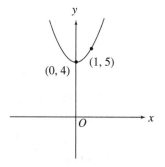

(0, 4)   (1, 5)

 11. If the figure above is the graph of $y = f(x)$, which of the following could be the equation of $f(x)$?

A) $f(x) = (x + 2)^2$

B) $f(x) = (x - 2)^2$

C) $f(x) = (x + 4)^2$

D) $f(x) = x^2 + 4$

Try plugging in points from the graph into the function.

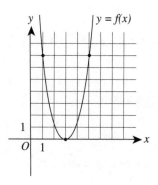

$y = f(x)$

17. If $g(x) = f\left(\dfrac{x}{3} - 1\right)$ and the graph of $f(x)$ is shown in the figure above, then what is the value of $g(6)$?

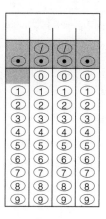

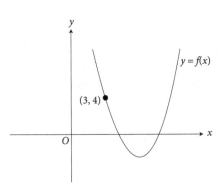

14. The figure above shows the graph of the quadratic function $f(x) = p(x - 5)^2 + q$, where p and q are constants. Which of the following number lines represents the range of all values of x that satisfy the equation $p(x - 5)^2 + q \leq 4$?

A) [number line with filled points at 3 and 7]

B) [number line with filled points at 5 and 8]

C) [number line with filled points at 3 and 7]

D) [number line with filled points at 5 and 7]

ROOTS, SOLUTIONS, ZEROS, AND *X*-INTERCEPTS

Believe it or not, all those are the exact same thing! We covered roots or solutions in the lesson on solving quadratics, but roots and *x*-intercepts also come into play on many functions and graphs questions.

10. If a linear function in the *xy*-plane has a slope of $-\dfrac{2}{7}$ and an *x*-intercept of 19, which of the following could be the equation of the function?

A) $y = -\dfrac{2}{7}x + \dfrac{38}{7}$

B) $y = -\dfrac{2}{7}x + \dfrac{46}{7}$

C) $y = -\dfrac{2}{7}x + 19$

D) $y = -\dfrac{2}{7}x + 23$

Whether they are called roots, solutions, zeros, or *x*-intercepts of the function, they are the *x*-values when $y = 0$. Look for opportunities to plug in or PITA.

23. The function f is defined by $f(x) = 2x^3 - x^2 + kx - 6$, where k is a constant. In the xy-plane, the graph of f intersects the x-axis at the three points $(3, 0)$, $(-\frac{1}{2}, 0)$, and $(q, 0)$. What is the value of k ?

A) −13

B) −2

C)   2

D) 13

What to do with all those points?

Since roots are the values for x that make $y = 0$, set the equation equal to 0, and solve for x. Other options include graphing the equation on your calculator or making your own sketch of the graph.

6. Which of the following could be the graph of the polynomial $y = (x^2 - 4x + 3)(x - 2)$?

Factor that quadratic!

A)

B)
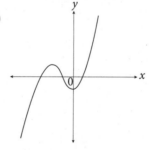

C)
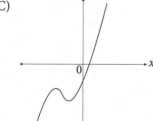

D)
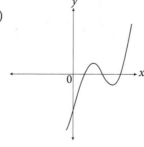

How does finding the roots help answer this question?

9. In the xy-plane, A and B are different points that have the same y-coordinate and are on the parabola given by $y = x^2 - 5x - 14$. What is the x-coordinate of the midpoint of $\overline{AB}$?

A) $\dfrac{2}{5}$

B) 1

C) $\dfrac{5}{2}$

D) $\dfrac{9}{2}$

Some questions may ask for the number of solutions to a system of equations. In this case, "solutions" refers any points shared by all the equations in the system.

$$y - x = 0$$
$$x^2 + y^2 = 1$$
$$y = 2x^3$$

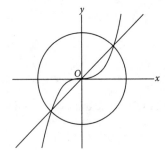

32. A system of three equations and their graphs in the xy-plane are shown in the figure above. How many solutions does this system have?

COORDINATE GEOMETRY

Now that you know all about functions in the xy-plane, let's cover a few related topics about coordinate geometry, which deals with lines, functions, and shapes in the xy-plane.

Slope-Intercept Form

The equation of a line in the xy-plane can be written in slope-intercept form, which is $y = mx + b$, where m is the slope and b is the y-intercept. The x and the y in the form represent the coordinates of any point on the line. This form is very useful for seeing how the line angles through the xy-plane and where it crosses the y-axis.

 19. If c is a constant less than 0, which of the following could be the graph of $y = 2c(x + y)$ in the xy-plane?

Plug in a value for c.

A)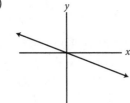

B)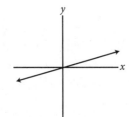

C)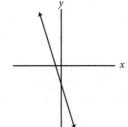

D)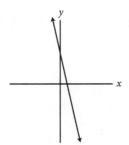

Sometimes, it is necessary to calculate the slope of a line.

 9. If $f(x)$ is a linear function such that $f(0) = 3$ and $f(1) = 6$, what is the slope of the graph of $y = f(x)$?

A) -3

B) $-\dfrac{1}{3}$

C) $\dfrac{1}{3}$

D) 3

$$\text{Slope} = \frac{y_2 - y_1}{x_2 - x_1}$$

Eliminate graphs that do not have the correct slope or y-intercept.

Parallel and Perpendicular Lines

Knowing the slope of a line is essential in determining if that line is parallel or perpendicular to a second line. Parallel lines have the same slope and no solutions, and perpendicular lines have one solution and slopes that are negative reciprocals. ETS often makes slope harder to see by giving answer choices that are not in slope-intercept form.

8. Which of the following is the equation of a line parallel to the line with equation $4x - 3y = 12$?

A) $12x - 9y = -15$

B) $4x - 4y = 16$

C) $4x + 3y = 12$

D) $3x + 4y = 15$

What does your POOD tell you to do with this question?

27. In the xy-plane, line m passes through the origin and is perpendicular to the line $8x - 3y = n$, where n is a constant. If the two lines intersect at the point $(r, r - 2)$, what is the value of r ?

A) $-\dfrac{11}{16}$

B) $\dfrac{3}{11}$

C) $\dfrac{11}{16}$

D) $\dfrac{16}{11}$

Parallel lines have the same slope and no solutions.
Perpendicular lines have negative reciprocal slopes and one solution.

Distance and Midpoint

Some questions will ask about the distance between two points that line in a plane. The distance formula can do this, of course, but if you forget it at test time, draw a right triangle with the points as the ends of the hypotenuse, and use the Pythagorean theorem to find the distance between them.

3. In the *xy*-plane, what is the distance from (5, 3) to (2, 7) ?

    A) 3

    B) 4

    C) 5

    D) 6

Look for 3:4:5, 6:8:10, and 5:12:13 triangles— ETS loves them! They may also use the 7:24:25 triangle once in a while.

 16. $\overline{AB}$ is the diameter of a circle that lies in the *xy*-plane. If the coordinates of point *A* are (5, 9) and those of *B* are (17, 17), what is the sum of the *x*- and *y*-coordinates of the center of the circle?

    A) 11

    B) 12

    C) 13

    D) 24

To find the **distance** between two points, make a right triangle, and use Pythagorean theorem.

To find the **midpoint** between two points, average the *x*-coordinates, and average the *y*-coordinates.

READING

WRITING AND LANGUAGE

MATH

ESSAY

FUNCTIONS AND GRAPHS DRILL
Time: 10 minutes

Unless you are aiming for a top score, don't try all the questions! Use your POOD to choose the best ones for you.

5

On a recent hiking trip in the High Atlas Mountains, Mackenzie starts her trek one morning from a basecamp that is 2,000 feet above sea level. If she ascends an additional 300 feet from sea level every hour, then which of the following functions accurately describes Mackenzie's altitude, A, in feet, as a function of her time in hours, t?

A) $h(t) = 2,000 + \dfrac{300}{t}$

B) $h(t) = 2,000 + 300t$

C) $h(t) = 300t - 2,000$

D) $h(t) = 2,000t + 300$

7

For all values of x, if the function $f(x)$ is defined as $f(x) = \dfrac{x}{2}$, then which of the following is the value of $f(2a - 4b)$?

A) $a + 2b$

B) $\dfrac{a - b}{4}$

C) $a - 4b$

D) $a - 2b$

11

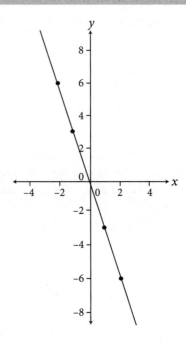

If the graph above describes the equation $y + x = k(y - x)$, what is the value of the constant k?

A) -3

B) $-\dfrac{1}{2}$

C) $\dfrac{1}{2}$

D) 3

13

If $f(x) = 3 - 4x$, what is the value of the expression $-2f(-2) - 3f(-3)$?

A) −67

B) −37

C) −17

D)   37

21

Andrea and Spiros decide to draw a map of the locations of their respective houses using the rectangular coordinate plane. They decide to place their high school at the origin and north on the positive y-axis. In order to walk to her house from school, Andrea must walk 1 mile east and 1.5 miles north. In order to walk to his house from school, Spiros must walk 0.75 miles west and 1.75 miles south. If each integer on the x- and y-axes of the coordinate plane represents one mile, then what are the coordinates of the midpoint between Andrea's and Spiros' houses?

A) $\left(-\dfrac{1}{8}, \dfrac{1}{8}\right)$

B) $\left(\dfrac{1}{8}, \dfrac{3}{8}\right)$

C) $\left(\dfrac{1}{8}, -\dfrac{1}{8}\right)$

D) $\left(\dfrac{3}{8}, \dfrac{1}{8}\right)$

25

$A(x)$ is a linear function such that $A(2) = 11$ and $A(-4) = -13$. If a second linear function, $B(x)$, is perpendicular to $A(x)$ and has a y-intercept of −2, then what is the x-intercept of $B(x)$?

A) $(-8, 0)$

B) $\left(-\dfrac{3}{4}, 0\right)$

C) $(0, 3)$

D) $(0, -2)$

35

In the function $f(x) = 3x^2 + 4x - 7$, for how many integer values of x between −3 and 3 is $f(x) \le 0$?

Summary

- Given a function, you put _____ in and get _____ out.

- For **word problems** containing functions, read carefully for _____, and look for ways to _____.

- For questions about the **graphs** of functions, remember that $f(x) = $ ____.
  - What can you do if the graph contains a labeled point?

  _____

- What are three other names for the **roots** of a function?

  _____

  _____

  - At the root, $y = $ ____.
  - To find the roots, you can
    _____,
    _____, or
    _____.

- What is the formula for the **slope** of a line?

  _____

  - **Parallel** slopes are
    _____.

  - **Perpendicular** slopes are
    _____

    _____.

- How do you find the **distance** between two points?

  _____

- How do you find the **midpoint** between two points?

  _____

- I have accomplished _____ of the _____ goals stated in the Introduction chapter.

ADVANCED FUNCTIONS AND GRAPHS

"Less is only more where more is no good."

–Frank Lloyd Wright

Seeing Things?

Look at the picture below. What do you see?

How many of you saw a rabbit? How many of you saw a duck? What are some other times in life in which it may be possible to look at the same situation in multiple ways?

Goals Review

At the conclusion of this chapter, you will be able to accomplish the following:

- Understand *how* to solve questions about even, odd, and compound functions
- Understand *how* to manipulate equations into the most useful form
- Understand *how* to transform graphs
- Understand *how* to handle questions about graphs of data

Advanced Functions and Graphs

In the previous Functions and Graphs chapter, we covered the basics of solving these questions. Of course, ETS may test some functions and graphing topics that are more advanced. Things like compound functions and transformation of graphs are less common, but still important if you are aiming high. This chapter will give you the skills you need to tackle these questions to get a top score.

ODD OR NOT?

ETS may ask if a function is even or odd. Even functions have symmetry across the y-axis, because every positive x-value yields the same y-value as the corresponding negative x-value. All functions with only even exponents fit into this category, though they are not the only even functions. Similarly, odd functions include those that contain only odd exponents (and no constants), plus a few others. Odd functions are symmetrical about the origin.

A function is **even** if $f(-x) = f(x)$. It has y-axis symmetry.

A function is **odd** if $f(-x) = -f(x)$. It has origin symmetry.

12. If an even function is one for which $f(x)$ and $f(-x)$ are equal, which of the following is an even function?

A) $h(x) = -x$

B) $h(x) = -|x|$

C) $h(x) = \dfrac{x}{2}$

D) $h(x) = 3x + 4$

Start plugging in!

COMPOUND FUNCTIONS

A compound function is a combination of two or more functions, in sequence. It's basically a function of a function—the output from the first function is the input for the second function. Start with the innermost part, and work your way out.

Work from the inside out on compound functions.

 18. If $f(x) = 5 - 2x$ and $g(x) = \dfrac{1}{x^2}$, what is the value of $f(g(-2))$?

A) $\dfrac{1}{81}$

B) 1

C) $\dfrac{9}{2}$

D) $\dfrac{9}{5}$

Look for ways to plug in on compound functions.

 25. If $g(x) = \dfrac{x^2}{4}$ and $f(g(x)) = \dfrac{x}{2}$, which of the following could be $f(x)$?

A) $\sqrt{x}$

B) $\sqrt{2x}$

C) x

D) x^2

FORMS OF EQUATIONS

The equation of a parabola can come in many forms. Many questions will give the equation in the standard form of $y = ax^2 + bx + c$. Another useful form is the vertex form. Knowing the vertex of a parabola can help you more easily answer questions about the minimum or maximum value a parabolic function will reach or the x-value that results in that minimum or maximum y-value.

The **vertex form** of a parabola is $y = a(x - h)^2 + k$, where (h, k) is the vertex.

To convert a parabola equation in the standard form of $y = ax^2 + bx + c$ to the vertex form, complete the square.

1. Make $y = 0$, and move any constants over to the left side of the equation.

2. If the value of a (the coefficient on the x^2 term) is anything other than 1, factor that value out of the right side of the equation.

3. Take half the value of b (the coefficient on the x-term, including the sign), square it, and add the result on the right side of the equation within the parentheses and the result times a to the left side of the equation.

4. Convert the right side of the equation to square form: $(x - h)^2$.

5. Move the value on the left side of the equation back over to the right side. Then, put y back in on the left side.

10. Suzanne sells homemade jewelry online. She finds that if she sets the price too low or too high, she loses money. Her net profit, in hundreds of dollars, is represented by the equation $n(p) = -3p^2 + 42p - 120$, where p represents the price at which she sells her jewelry. Which of the following equivalent forms of this equation would be most useful in determining the price at which Suzanne could maximize her profit?

A) $n(p) = -3p^2 + 42p - 120$

B) $n(p) = -3(p^2 - 14p + 40)$

C) $n(p) = -3(p - 4)(p - 10)$

D) $n(p) = -3(p - 7)^2 + 27$

Circle equations in the xy-plane also have a standard form, and ETS likes to ask questions about circles in non-standard form. Just as with parabolas, knowing the parts of the standard form and how to manipulate circle equations into different forms can be useful.

> The **standard form** of a circle is $(x - h)^2 + (y - k)^2 = r^2$, where (h, k) is the center, and r is the radius. If the circle is centered at the origin, the equation becomes $x^2 + y^2 = r^2$.
>
> To convert a circle equation into the standard form, complete the square.
>
> 1. Move any constants over to the right side of the equation.
> 2. Take half of the coefficient on the x-term (not the x^2 term), including the sign, square it, and add it to both sides of the equation.
> 3. Convert the x^2 term, the x-term, and the constant on the left to square form: $(x - h)^2$.
> 4. Repeat steps 2 and 3 with the y-terms.

7. In the xy-plane, if the point $(1, 3)$ is on circle M, and circle M has a radius of 4, which of the following equations could describe circle M?

   A) $(x - 2)^2 + (y + 3)^2 = 16$

   B) $(x - 1)^2 + (y + 1)^2 = 16$

   C) $(x - 1)^2 + (y - 3)^2 = 4$

   D) $(x - 5)^2 + (y - 3)^2 = 4$

 20. Which of the following represents the center and the radius, respectively, of the circle described by the equation $x^2 + y^2 - 8x + 6y = -21$ graphed in the xy-plane?

   A) Center: $(-4, 3)$, radius: 2

   B) Center: $(-4, 3)$, radius: 4

   C) Center: $(4, -3)$, radius: 2

   D) Center: $(4, -3)$, radius: 4

TRANSFORMATION OF GRAPHS

Occasionally, a question will ask about a transformation of a graph. Although this may conjure images of Optimus Prime, it is not nearly so exciting. Graph transformation means the function has been changed in some way, either moved up, down, or side-to-side, or sometimes flipped over, stretched, or squashed.

In relation to $f(x)$:

- $f(x) + c$ is shifted upward c units in the xy-plane
- $f(x) - c$ is shifted downward c units in the xy-plane
- $f(x + c)$ is shifted to the left c units in the xy-plane
- $f(x - c)$ is shifted to the right c units in the xy-plane
- $-f(x)$ is flipped upside down over the x-axis
- $f(-x)$ is flipped left-right over the y-axis
- $|f(x)|$ is the result of flipping upward all the parts of the graph that appear below the x-axis
- $a \cdot f(x)$ widens the graph if $|a| < 1$ and narrows the graph if $|a| > 1$

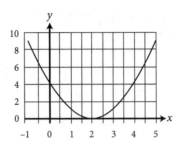

Take it one transformation at a time, and use POE.

16. The graph of the function $f(x) = (x - 2)^2$ is shown above. A second function, $g(x)$, is given by the equation $g(x) = -f(x) + 2$. Which of the following best represents the graph of $g(x)$?

A)

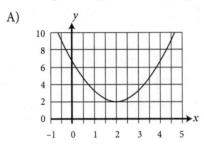

B)

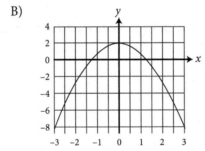

C)

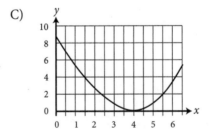

D)

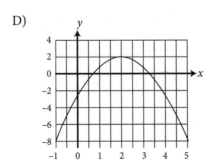

GRAPHS OF SINE AND COSINE

ETS may ask about the graph of a sine or a cosine wave or about the transformation of these functions. It is helpful to know what the graphs look like without any transformations.

$y = \sin \theta$

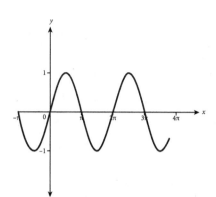

$y = \cos \theta$

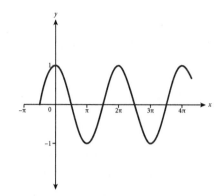

The amplitude of the wave, or the number of units the graph goes above or below the midline, is indicated by the number in front of the function.

$y = 2\sin \theta$

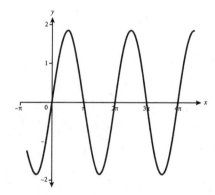

$y = \dfrac{1}{2} \cos \theta$

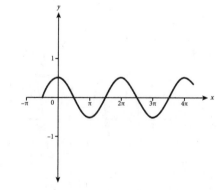

The period of the wave, or how far the wave travels before it repeats itself, is determined by the number in front of the x or θ. The standard period is 2π.

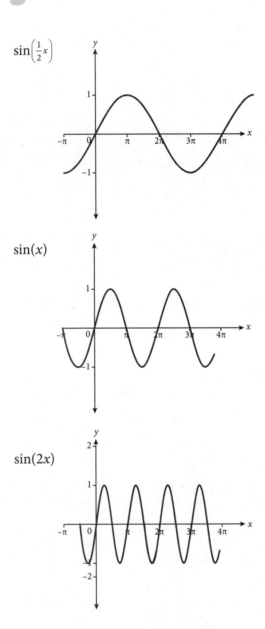

And, of course, these waves can be moved up or down, like any other function, by adding or subtracting a number outside the parentheses.

GRAPHING AND DATA ANALYSIS

Graphing skills can also help on some Data Analysis questions. Ones that ask for the line or curve of best fit are really just asking for the slope or the equation of the function.

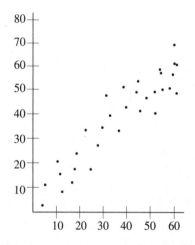

 13. Which of the following best approximates the slope of the line that best fits the scatterplot above?

    A) −1

    B)   1

    C)   2

    D)   5

Plug in points or ballpark.

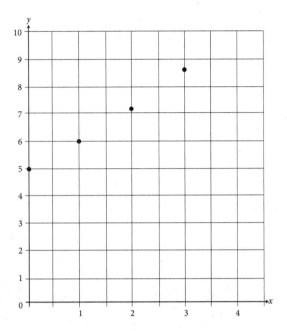

Plug in points!

17. The above graph shows the hourly growth of a certain bacteria. A scientist noted that at the beginning of the experiment, there were five bacteria in the petri dish. After one hour, the bacteria had increased to six. The growth continues to increase exponentially over time. If x represents the hours since the beginning of the experiments and $f(x)$ represents the number of bacteria in the petri dish at that given hour, which of the following graphs could represent the equation of the bacteria's growth?

A) $f(x) = 2x + 4$

B) $f(x) = 2x^2 + 5$

C) $f(x) = 5(1 + 0.2)^x$

D) $f(x) = 5(1 + 0.3)^x$

Sketch a graph of each answer choice, and use POE.

22. Which of the following, if represented graphically, would illustrate a pattern of linear growth?

A) In a certain country, each person has an average of two children. Thirty years later, each of those two children has two children. Thirty years later, each of those four resulting children has two children, and so forth.

B) A scientist places a bacterial sample in a petri dish and observes what happens over time. She observes that the first organism splits into two daughter organisms, which then split to form four organisms, which then split to form eight organisms.

C) A taxicab company that typically transports people back and forth from the airport charges customers a base fee of $3 and an additional $0.25 for each mile of driving.

D) Each month, a credit card company charges 2% interest on the amount that an individual owes, and that interest is added back to the amount that the individual owes. This process is repeated every month.

ADVANCED FUNCTIONS DRILL

Time: 10 minutes

Unless you are aiming for a top score, don't try all the questions! Use your POOD to choose the best ones for you.

3

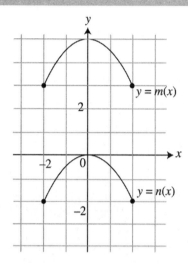

The complete graphs of the functions m and n are shown in the xy-plane above. Which of the following could be equal to $n(x)$?

A) $m(x + 5)$

B) $m(x - 5)$

C) $m(x) + 5$

D) $m(x) - 5$

17

If $f(x) = \dfrac{x}{3}$ and $g(x) = 3f(x) + 2$, then what is the value of $g(9)$?

12

If an odd function is one for which $f(-x) = -f(x)$, which of the following is NOT an odd function?

A) $f(x) = 3x^3$

B) $f(x) = (x - 2)^5$

C) $f(x) = -4x$

D) $f(x) = \sin x$

15

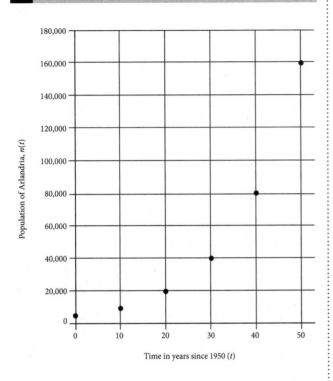

Population of Arlandria, $n(t)$

Time in years since 1950 (t)

The graph above shows the growth in population of the city of Arlandria from the year 1950 to the year 2000. If $n(t)$ represents the number of people living in Arlandria and t represents the time, in years, since 1950, then which of the following functions could accurately represent Arlandria's population growth in the second half of the twentieth century?

A) $n(t) = 5,000\left(\dfrac{2}{t}\right)^{10}$

B) $n(t) = 5,000\left(2\right)^{\frac{t}{10}}$

C) $n(t) = 5,000(2t)$

D) $n(t) = 5,000(2t^2)$

19

The parabola $y = x^2$ has been shifted so that its minimum is now located at the point $(2, 0)$ on the xy-plane. The equation of the shifted parabola can be given by $y = M^2$. What is the expression for M?

A) x^2

B) $2x - 2$

C) $x - 2$

D) $x + 2$

35

If the equation $f(x) = x^2 + 6x + 12$ is converted into the vertex form, $f(x) = a(x - h)^2 + k$, then what is the value of k?

28

A circle (not shown) has its center at the point (–3, –2) and is tangent to the y-axis. Which of the following points lies outside the circle?

A) (–5, 1)

B) (–4, –2)

C) (–2, 0)

D) (0, –2)

Summary

- If $f(-x) = f(x)$, the functions is _____ and has _____ symmetry.

- If $f(-x) = -f(x)$, the function is _____ and has _____ symmetry.

- On **compound function** questions, work _____ and look for ways to _____.

- What is the **vertex form** of a parabola?

  _____

- What is the **standard form** of a circle?

  _____

- How do you get equations into these forms if necessary?

  _____

- When a function undergoes more than one **transformation**, remember to _____ and to use _____.

- Which skills are useful on **Data Analysis** questions about graphs of functions?

  _____

  _____

- I have accomplished _____ of the _____ goals stated in the Introduction chapter.

ADDITIONAL TOPICS

"I guess a sock is also a geometric shape—technically—
but I don't know what you'd call it. A socktagon?"

–Stephen King

Reference Information

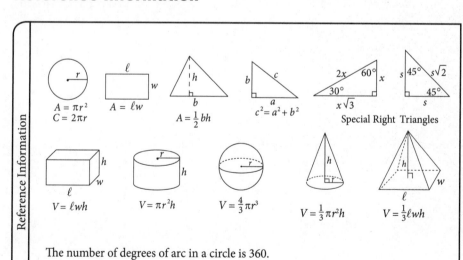

Trivia Night!

In what city is the Blue Mosque located? Which American Founding Father founded the University of Virginia? In what year was the first SAT administered? You probably have a friend (or maybe it's you) who is a "trivia geek" and loves to remember all of these minute details. However, how important is it to remember all of these random pieces of information?

Goals Review

At the conclusion of this chapter, you will be able to accomplish the following:

- Understand *how* to use the Geometry Basic Approach on all geometry problems
- Understand *how* to solve questions related to lines and angles
- Understand *how* to solve questions related to triangles and circles
- Understand *when* and *how* to tackle advanced math topics

What's an Additional Topic?

This chapter covers some odds and ends, including concepts cleverly named "Additional Topics" by ETS (geometry and complex numbers) and some weird things like the meaning of a variable or constant in context. What these all have in common is that these questions are not in every student's POOD. There are a lot of topics covered here, but there are only 6 Additional Topics questions on the test —3 in the Calculator section and 3 in the No-Calculator section. Choose wisely which—if any—of these questions to tackle on the test.

GEOMETRY

As with many other questions in the Math sections of the SAT, keeping the information organized and having a plan of attack will help with the geometry questions.

Geometry Basic Approach

1. **Draw** a figure if one is not provided.
2. **Label** all information from the question on the figure.
3. **Write** the complete formula on the paper.
4. **Ballpark** if possible.

Let's start by practicing the first step—draw your own figure based on the following descriptions.

An equilateral triangle

An isosceles right triangle

A rectangular solid

A line tangent to a circle

A chord in a circle

A circle inscribed in a square

Now use that last shape to practice applying the Basic Approach to the following geometry question.

10. If a square has an area of x, then, in terms of x, what is the circumference of the largest circle that can be inscribed in the square?

A) $\pi \sqrt{x}$

B) $\dfrac{\pi \sqrt{x}}{2}$

C) πx^2

D) $\dfrac{\pi x}{4}$

Apply the first three steps of the Basic Approach to all geometry problems. However, if you get STUCK…

GEOMETRY BALLPARKING

As long as the diagram doesn't say, "Note: Figure not drawn to scale." below it, you can Ballpark to eliminate incorrect answers. Answers that don't agree with the figure *cannot* be correct.

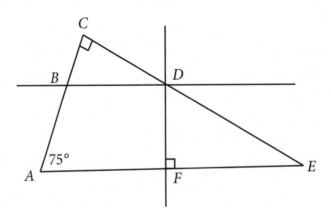

Ballpark!

6. In the figure above, $\angle CAE$ measures 75°, and $\overline{AE}$ is parallel to $\overline{BD}$. What is the measure of $\angle CDF$?

A)   15°

B)   75°

C)   90°

D)   105°

LINES AND ANGLES

Many geometry questions about lines will be about parallel or perpendicular lines. Questions about angles are often about congruent angles, right angles, or two angles that add up to 90º.

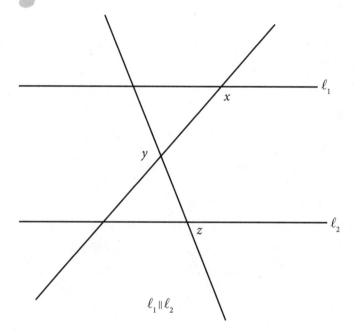

When parallel lines are intersected by the same line, two kinds of angles are created—BIG and small.

BIG ANGLES = BIG ANGLES. small angles = small angles.

BIG + small = 180 degrees.

7. In the figure above, $x = 120°$ and $y = 110°$. What is the measure of z, in degrees?

A) 10

B) 30

C) 50

D) 70

Label the information on the figure.

TRIANGLES

Triangle questions on the SAT will cover some of these ideas about lines and angles, as well as other topics such as trigonometry and similarity.

TRIGONOMETRY

The SAT—now with Trig! Knowing the basic definitions of sine, cosine, and tangent will be helpful in solving some questions about right triangles.

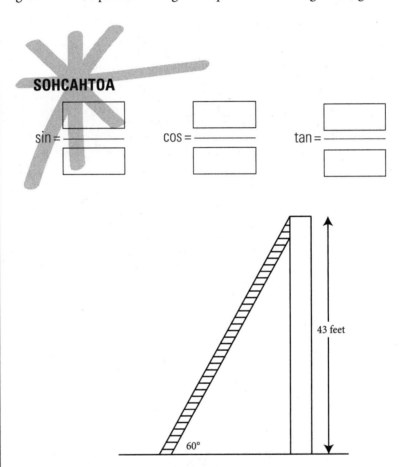

SOHCAHTOA

$$\sin = \frac{\boxed{}}{\boxed{}} \qquad \cos = \frac{\boxed{}}{\boxed{}} \qquad \tan = \frac{\boxed{}}{\boxed{}}$$

43 feet

60°

17. The figure above shows a ladder leaned against a wall so that the top of the ladder touches the top of the wall. The ladder is placed so that the base is at a 60° angle to the ground. If the wall is 43 feet tall, what is the length of the ladder, to the nearest foot?

    A) 25

    B) 50

    C) 75

    D) 85

RADIANS AND DEGREES

Radians and degrees are different ways of measuring angles. Your calculator has both modes, so make sure to use the right mode when calculating anything. Sometimes, ETS will ask you to convert degrees to radians or vice versa.

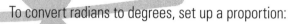

To convert radians to degrees, set up a proportion:

$$\frac{\pi}{180} = \frac{\text{radians}}{\text{degrees}}$$

11. An angle measures $-\dfrac{5\pi}{8}$ radians. What is the measure of the angle, in degrees?

A) −247.5

B) −125.0

C) −112.5

D) 247.5

On the No-Calculator section, ETS may ask about the relationship between sine and cosine of the complementary angles of a right triangle. Use the formulas below to solve these.

$$\sin x = \cos\left(\frac{\pi}{2} - x\right) \text{ and } \cos x = \sin\left(\frac{\pi}{2} - x\right)$$

9. Which of the following is equal to $\sin\left(\dfrac{\pi}{7}\right)$?

A) $\sin\left(\dfrac{5\pi}{14}\right)$

B) $\cos\left(\dfrac{5\pi}{14}\right)$

C) $-\sin\left(\dfrac{\pi}{7}\right)$

D) $-\cos\left(\dfrac{\pi}{7}\right)$

PYTHAGOREAN THEOREM

If two sides of a right triangle are given, the third side can be found using the Pythagorean theorem. ETS loves to use the Pythagorean triples, though, so be on the lookout for 3:4:5, 6:8:10, 5:12:13, or even 7:24:25 triangles. Knowing them can save time.

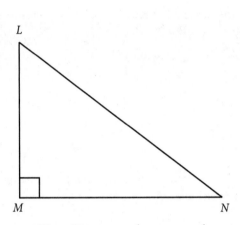

Pythagorean theorem: $a^2 + b^2 = c^2$, where c is the hypotenuse.

Note: Figure not drawn to scale.

Look for Pythagorean triples!

21. In the figure above, if $\overline{MN} = 6$, and $\tan \angle MLN = \dfrac{12}{5}$, what is the length of $\overline{LN}$?

A) 6.5

B) 12

C) 13

D) 26

Sometimes, ETS will hide a right triangle in a diagram and ask a trigonometry question about the given shape. Look for a way to make a right triangle, and use SOHCAHTOA.

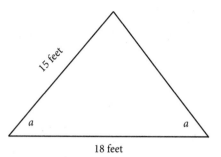

15 feet

18 feet

a a

35. Tom sketches out the above diagram for the sail of a boat he is building. What is the value of sin a ?

What line can be drawn to make this into two right triangles?

SPECIAL RIGHT TRIANGLES

In addition to Pythagorean triples, be on the lookout for special right triangles—ETS loves 30°:60°:90° and 45°:45°:90° triangles. They include information about the relationship of the sides of these triangles in the reference box at the start of each section. Recognizing them and using those relationships can help you skip the step of using the Pythagorean theorem to find the missing side.

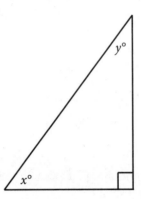

How do you know this is a special right triangle?

7. In the figure above, the measure of angle y is equal to $\dfrac{\pi}{6}$ radians. Which of the following is equal to $\sin x$?

A) $\dfrac{1}{2}$

B) 1

C) 2

D) $\dfrac{\sqrt{3}}{2}$

SIMILAR TRIANGLES

Two triangles are similar if the three angles in the first triangle are the same as the three angles in the second triangle. Similar means "same shape, different size."

The corresponding sides of two similar triangles are proportional in length.

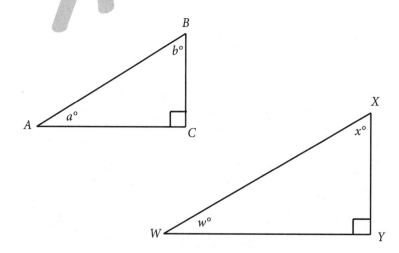

8. In the figure above, if $\sin a = \dfrac{1}{2}$ and $b = x$, what is the value of $\sin x$?

A) $\dfrac{1}{2}$

B) $\dfrac{\sqrt{3}}{2}$

C) $\dfrac{\sqrt{3}}{3}$

D) $\sqrt{3}$

CIRCLES

Aside from basic circle questions about circumference and area, ETS may ask about a slice of a circle (a sector) or a part of the circumference (an arc).

Arcs and sectors are proportional to the central angle of a circle.

$$\frac{\text{part}}{\text{whole}} = \frac{\text{central angle}}{360°} = \frac{\text{arc length}}{2\pi r} = \frac{\text{sector area}}{\pi r^2}$$

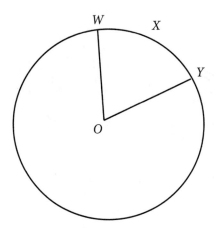

Note: Figure not drawn to scale.

10. The figure above shows a circle with center O. The central angle described by $\overarc{WXY}$ measures $\frac{\pi}{4}$ radians. If the circle has a radius of 5, what is the length of $\overarc{WXY}$?

    A) $\frac{3\pi}{4}$

    B) π

    C) $\frac{5\pi}{4}$

    D) $\frac{3\pi}{2}$

To find an arc length of a circle in radians, use $s = r\theta$

DARN THAT ETS!

The following topics are the ones that can be the trickiest on the SAT, though some questions are easier than others. Use your POOD to decide whether or not to tackle these advanced concepts, and try to Ballpark or Plug In whenever possible. Remember to use your LOTD on any questions you skip.

OVERLAPPING SHAPES

When given one shape inside another, use the information given about the first shape to determine the necessary information about the second shape. Sometimes, it may be necessary to draw a line that means something to both shapes, such as a diameter of a circle that is the diagonal of an inscribed square.

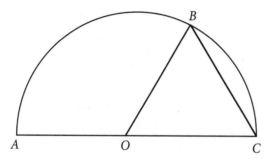

 20. In the figure above, $\triangle OBC$ is inscribed in a semicircle with center O. If the length of minor arc $\overset{\frown}{BC}$ is 2π and the area of the semicircle is 18π, what is the length of side $\overline{BC}$ of the triangle?

A) 3

B) 6

C) $6\sqrt{3}$

D) 12

VOLUME

Try following the Basic Approach on these volume questions.

Variables in the answers?
Plug in!

22. A rectangular solid has a width of x inches, a length of $2x$ inches, and a height of x^2 inches. If a piece with a volume of 4 cubic inches is removed from the solid, what is the resulting volume of the solid, in terms of x ?

A) $x(3 + x) - 4$

B) $3x^2 - 4$

C) $4(x^2 - 1)$

D) $2(x^4 - 2)$

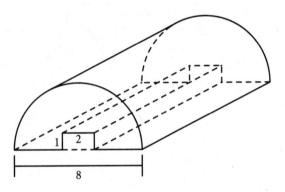

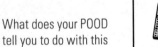

What does your POOD tell you to do with this question?

29. The figure above shows a semicircular plastic cover used to hide an electrical cord run along a wall. The plastic cover has a groove cut out of its base in the shape of a rectangular solid. The diameter of the semicircular plastic cover is 8 cm, while the groove is 1 cm high and 2 cm wide. The cover and the groove cut out of it are both 10 cm in length. The plastic has a density of 1.25 grams per cubic centimeter. What is the mass of the plastic cover, with the groove cut out, to the nearest gram? (Density is mass divided by volume.)

A) 289

B) 315

C) 482

D) 603

COMPLEX NUMBERS

Occasionally, a mathematical operation will require taking a square root of a negative number. With real numbers, that isn't possible—no real number can be squared to get a negative number. This is where i comes in. The i stands for "imaginary," to distinguish it from "real" numbers, and it equals $\sqrt{-1}$. When i is squared, the result is –1. "Complex numbers" combine real and imaginary numbers in the form $a + bi$, where a is real, and bi is imaginary.

The **imaginary number** $i = \sqrt{-1}$.

Treat i just like a variable, except that $i^2 = -1$.

$a + bi$ is a **complex number**, where a is real, and bi is imaginary.

Many calculators have an i button and an $a + bi$ mode.

$$1 - i + i^2 - i^3$$

6. Which of the following is equivalent to the above expression?

(Note: $i = \sqrt{-1}$)

A) $-i$

B) -1

C) 0

D) i

Sometimes, solving questions with i is as simple as substituting –1 for i^2. On hard questions, it may be necessary to multiply the denominator's complex expression by its conjugate to make the i disappear.

$$\frac{i + 3}{i - 3}$$

9. Which of the following is equivalent to the above expression?
(Note: $i^2 = -1$)

A) $-\dfrac{4}{5} - \dfrac{3i}{5}$

B) $-\dfrac{4}{5} + \dfrac{3i}{5}$

C) $\dfrac{4}{5} - \dfrac{3i}{5}$

D) $\dfrac{4}{5} + \dfrac{3i}{5}$

Conjugate of a complex expression? Switch the sign on the imaginary part.

MEANING OF CONSTANT OR VARIABLE IN CONTEXT

Finally, there are some oddball questions ETS has decided to throw in that ask about the meaning of something in context. First, ask yourself if they should be in your POOD. If you are shooting for a top score and decide to try these, read the question carefully, and use this Basic Approach.

Meaning in Context Basic Approach

1) RTFQ: Underline key words, and identify which term the equation is asking about.

2) Label what you can within the equation provided based on your Bite-Sized Pieces.

3) POE what's inconsistent with your labels and the equation given.

4) Plug-and-Play: Plug in your own numbers to see if the story makes sense.

5) Use POE to try to get down to one answer choice, or guess and go.

---

7. To celebrate a coworker's retirement, all of the c employees of a company planned to contribute equally to the purchase of a retirement gift that cost d dollars. Later, k of the employees decided not to contribute. The additional amount, in dollars, that each of the remaining employees had to contribute is given by the expression $\dfrac{d}{c-k} - \dfrac{d}{c}$. Which of the following best describes what $\dfrac{d}{c}$ represents in this expression?

A) The total amount that all of the c employees originally planned to pay

B) The amount that each of the k employees will now pay toward the gift

C) The amount that each employee would have paid if all of the c employees had contributed equally

D) The amount that each employee had to pay after k employees decided not to contribute

$$\left(\frac{x}{3}\right)^2 + \left(\frac{x}{5}\right)^2 = \frac{1}{3}$$

10. Two fungal species of *Aspergillus flavus*, AF-36 and AF-42, were grown in liquid cultures at a temperature of 37° C and spun at 60 rotations per minute. The AF-36 culture grew at a slower rate than did the AF-42 culture, and together the cultures produced in 3 days the amount of fungus required for experiments. The equation above represents the experiment described. Which of the following describes what the expression $\left(\frac{x}{5}\right)^2$ represents in this equation?

A) The average amount of AF-36 fungus that is produced in one day

B) The time, in days, that it takes for AF-36 to produce the total amount of fungus alone

C) The time, in days, that it takes for AF-42 to produce the total amount of fungus alone

D) The average amount of AF-42 fungus that is produced in one day

ADDITIONAL TOPICS DRILL

Time: 10 minutes

Unless you are aiming for a top score, don't try all the questions! Use your POOD to choose the best ones for you.

32

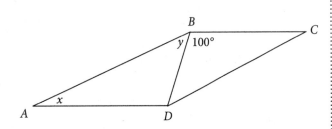

Note: Figure not drawn to scale.

In parallelogram *ABCD* above, *x* = 40° and ∠*DBC* = 100°. What is the value of 2*y* ?

5

Rebekah and Ian live 150 miles apart. Deciding to meet partway between their respective houses for a picnic, they both leave their houses at the same time and drive without stopping until they meet each other. Rebekah drives at an average speed of 50 miles per hour, and Ian drives at an average speed of 80 miles per hour. In the equation $50x + 80x = 150$, what does $80x$ represent?

A) The speed at which Rebekah drives

B) The speed at which Ian drives

C) The total distance that Rebekah drives

D) The total distance that Ian drives

8

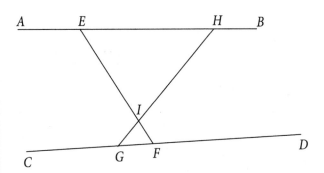

Note: Figure not drawn to scale.

In the figure above, $\overline{AB} \parallel \overline{CD}$. Which of the following must be true?

A) ∠*AEI* = ∠*BHI*

B) △*EIH* ~ △*FIG*

C) $\overline{EF} \perp \overline{GH}$

D) ∠*EIG* = ∠*EIH*

13

In a circle with center P (not shown), points Q, R, and S lie on the circumference. If $\overline{PR} = 7$ and $\angle QPS = 45°$, then what is the area of the minor sector PQS ?

A) $\dfrac{49\pi}{8}$

B) $\dfrac{49\pi}{4}$

C) 14π

D) 49π

10

While flying a kite with a string of length 90 feet, Lauren found that the wind kept her kite in the air at an average angle measure of 60° relative to the ground, but she was dissatisfied with how high the kite flew. She tried a different kite with a string of length 120 feet, and the wind continued to keep her new kite in the air at an average angle measure of 60° relative to the ground. How much higher (in vertical feet) did Lauren's second kite fly than her first kite flew?

A)   15.00

B)   25.98

C)   77.94

D)   103.92

27

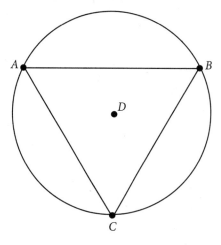

Note: Figure not drawn to scale.

In the circle with center D shown above, $\triangle ABC$ is equilateral and is inscribed in the circle. If $\overline{AD} = x$, then which of the following represents the length of $\overset{\frown}{BC}$, in terms of x ?

A) $\dfrac{\pi x}{6}$

B) $\dfrac{2\pi x}{3}$

C) $\dfrac{\pi x^2}{6}$

D) $\dfrac{2\pi x^2}{3}$

14

$$\left(\frac{2}{3}+\frac{5i}{3}\right)^2 - \left(\frac{2}{3}+\frac{i}{3}\right)^2$$

Which of the following is equivalent to the above expression?

(Note: $i^2 = -1$)

A) $-\dfrac{8}{3}$

B) $-\dfrac{8}{3} + \dfrac{8i}{3}$

C) $-\dfrac{8}{3} + \dfrac{16i}{9}$

D) $\dfrac{8}{3} - \dfrac{16i}{9}$

Summary

- What **four steps** should you follow for **all geometry questions**?

  _____

  _____

  _____

  _____

- What two kinds of angles are created when two **parallel lines** are both intersected by another line, and how are those angles related?

  _____

  _____

- What are the three key definitions in the mnemonic **SOHCAHTOA**?

  _____

  _____

  _____

- What is the formula you need to convert back and forth between **radians** and **degrees**?

  _____

- What is the formula that describes the relationship between the **sine** and **cosine** of **complementary angles** in a right triangle?

  _____

- What are the three **Pythagorean triples** that are commonly tested on the SAT?

  _____

  _____

  _____

- In what situation can two **triangles** be described as **similar**?

  _____

- What formulas can you use to express the **proportional relationship** between the various aspects of a **circle**?

  _____

  _____

  _____

- I have accomplished _____ of the _____ goals stated in the Introduction chapter.

ESSAY

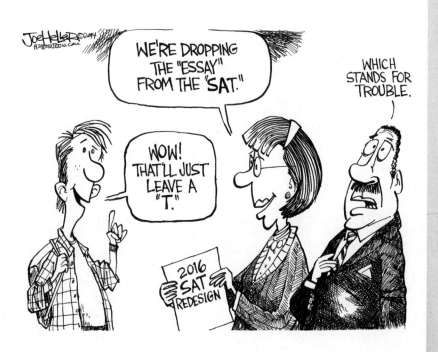

INTRODUCTION

ESSAY: INTRODUCTION

The final task on the SAT is to write a rhetorical analysis essay. You will have 50 minutes to read a text and write a logical, well-constructed analysis of the author's argument.

According to ETS, the essay will show:

> *"Students can demonstrate college and career readiness proficiency in producing a cogent and clear written analysis using evidence drawn from an appropriately challenging source text written for a broad audience."*

This really means:

> *Students can read an essay and explain specifics from the essay to show how the author builds his/her argument*

The prompt will be nearly the same every time, just with a different source text. The prompt will be something much like this:

As you read the passage below, consider how [the author] uses

- evidence, such as facts or examples, to support claims.
- reasoning to develop ideas and to connect claims and evidence.
- stylistic or persuasive elements, such as word choice or appeals to emotion, to add power to the ideas expressed.

[Source Text Will Appear Here]

Write an essay in which you explain how [the author] builds an argument to persuade [his/her] audience that [author's claim]. In your essay, analyze how [the author] uses one or more of the features listed above (or features of your own choice) to strengthen the logic and persuasiveness of [his/her] argument. Be sure that your analysis focuses on the most relevant aspects of the passage.

Your essay should not explain whether you agree with [the author's] claims, but rather explain how the author builds an argument to persuade [his/her] audience.

The Essay requires you to:
- Carefully read a text
- Understand how an author appeals to a reader's logic, emotions, or morals
- Write a logical analysis of an argument
- Explain how style choices can affect an author's persuasiveness

The Essay does NOT require you to:
- Give your opinion about a text
- Memorize examples from history or literature
- Have previous experience with the text

Two graders will read and score the essay on a 1-4 scale in three different categories (Reading, Analysis, and Writing).

4 = Advanced
3 = Proficient
2 = Partial
1 = Inadequate

You'll receive three scores for the SAT Essay—one for each dimension—ranging from 2–8 points. The scores will be determined using the following rubric:

ETS's Essay Rubric			
Score of 4: Advanced	**Score of 3: Proficient**	**Score of 2: Partial**	**Score of 1: Inadequate**
Reading • Demonstrates thorough comprehension of the source text. • Shows an understanding of the text's central idea(s) and of most important details and how they interrelate, demonstrating a comprehensive understanding of the text. • Is free of errors of fact or interpretation with regard to the text. • Makes skillful use of textual evidence (quotations, paraphrases, or both), demonstrating a complete understanding of the source text.	• Demonstrates effective comprehension of the source text. • Shows an understanding of the text's central idea(s) and important details. • Is free of substantive errors of fact and interpretation with regard to the text. • Makes appropriate use of textual evidence (quotations, paraphrases, or both), demonstrating an understanding of the source text.	• Demonstrates some comprehension of the source text. • Shows an understanding of the text's central idea(s) but not of important details. • May contain errors of fact and/or interpretation with regard to the text. • Makes limited and/or haphazard use of textual evidence (quotations, paraphrases, or both), demonstrating some understanding of the source text.	• Demonstrates little or no comprehension of the source text. • Fails to show an understanding of the text's central idea(s), and may include only details without reference to central idea(s). • May contain numerous errors of fact and/or interpretation with regard to the text. • Makes little or no use of textual evidence (quotations, paraphrases, or both), demonstrating little or no understanding of the source text.
Analysis • Offers an insightful analysis of the source text and demonstrates a sophisticated understanding of the analytical task. • Offers a thorough, well-considered evaluation of the author's use of evidence, reasoning, and/or stylistic and persuasive elements, and/or feature(s) of the student's own choosing. • Contains relevant, sufficient, and strategically chosen support for claim(s) or point(s) made. • Focuses consistently on those features of the text that are most relevant to addressing the task.	• Offers an effective analysis of the source text and demonstrates an understanding of the analytical task. • Competently evaluates the author's use of evidence, reasoning, and/or stylistic and persuasive elements, and/or feature(s) of the student's own choosing. • Contains relevant and sufficient support for claim(s) or point(s) made. • Focuses primarily on those features of the text that are most relevant to addressing the task.	• Offers limited analysis of the source text and demonstrates only partial understanding of the analytical task. • Identifies and attempts to describe the author's use of evidence, reasoning, and/or stylistic and persuasive elements, and/or feature(s) of the student's own choosing, but merely asserts rather than explains their importance, or one or more aspects of the response's analysis are unwarranted based on the text. • Contains little or no support for claim(s) or point(s) made. • May lack a clear focus on those features of the text that are most relevant to addressing the task.	• Offers little or no analysis or ineffective analysis of the source text and demonstrates little or no understanding of the analytic task. • Identifies without explanation some aspects of the author's use of evidence, reasoning, and/or stylistic and persuasive elements, and/or feature(s) of the student's choosing, • Numerous aspects of the response's analysis are unwarranted based on the text, • Contains little or no support for claim(s) or point(s) made, or support is largely irrelevant. • May not focus on features of the text that are relevant to addressing the task or the response offers no discernible analysis (e.g., is largely or exclusively summary).

Writing			
• Cohesive and demonstrates a highly effective use and command of language. • Includes a precise central claim. • Includes a skillful introduction and conclusion. The response demonstrates a deliberate and highly effective progression of ideas both within paragraphs and throughout the essay. • Wide variety in sentence structures. The response demonstrates a consistent use of precise word choice. The response maintains a formal style and objective tone. • Shows a strong command of the conventions of standard written English and is free or virtually free of errors.	• Mostly cohesive and demonstrates effective use and control of language. • Includes a central claim or implicit controlling idea. • Includes an effective introduction and conclusion. The response demonstrates a clear progression of ideas both within paragraphs and throughout the essay. • Variety in sentence structures. The response demonstrates some precise word choice. The response maintains a formal style and objective tone. • Shows a good control of the conventions of standard written English and is free of significant errors that detract from the quality of writing.	• Demonstrates little or no cohesion and limited skill in the use and control of language. • May lack a clear central claim or controlling idea or may deviate from the claim or idea over the course of the response. • May include an ineffective introduction and/or conclusion. The response may demonstrate some progression of ideas within paragraphs but not throughout the response. • Limited variety in sentence structures; sentence structures may be repetitive. • Demonstrates general or vague word choice; word choice may be repetitive. The response may deviate noticeably from a formal style and objective tone. • Shows a limited control of the conventions of standard written English and contains errors that detract from the quality of writing and may impede understanding.	• Demonstrates little or no cohesion and inadequate skill in the use and control of language. • May lack a clear central claim or controlling idea. • Lacks a recognizable introduction and conclusion. The response does not have a discernible progression of ideas. • Lacks variety in sentence structures; sentence structures may be repetitive. The response demonstrates general and vague word choice; word choice may be poor or inaccurate. The response may lack a formal style and objective tone. • Shows a weak control of the conventions of standard written English and may contain numerous errors that undermine the quality of writing.

Let's take a look at some sample essays.

As you read the passage below, consider how Kennedy uses

- evidence, such as facts or examples, to support claims.
- reasoning to develop ideas and to connect claims and evidence.
- stylistic or persuasive elements, such as word choice or appeals to emotion, to add power to the ideas expressed.

John F. Kennedy. September 12, 1962. Rice Stadium, Houston, TX

1   We set sail on this new sea because there is new knowledge to be gained, and new rights to be won, and they must be won and used for the progress of all people. For space science, like nuclear science and all technology, has no conscience of its own. Whether it will become a force for good or ill depends on man, and only if the United States occupies a position of pre-eminence can we help decide whether this new ocean will be a sea of peace or a new terrifying theater of war. I do not say the we should or will go unprotected against the hostile misuse of space any more than we go unprotected against the hostile use of land or sea, but I do say that space can be explored and mastered without feeding the fires of war, without repeating the mistakes that man has made in extending his writ around this globe of ours.

2   There is no strife, no prejudice, no national conflict in outer space as yet. Its hazards are hostile to us all. Its conquest deserves the best of all mankind, and its opportunity for peaceful cooperation may never come again. But why, some say, the moon? Why choose this as our goal? And they may well ask why climb the highest mountain? Why, 35 years ago, fly the Atlantic? Why does Rice play Texas?

3   We choose to go to the moon. We choose to go to the moon in this decade and do the other things, not because they are easy, but because they are hard, because that goal will serve to organize and measure the best of our energies and skills, because that challenge is one that we are willing to accept, one we are unwilling to postpone, and one which we intend to win, and the others, too.

4   It is for these reasons that I regard the decision last year to shift our efforts in space from low to high gear as among the most important decisions that will be made during my incumbency in the office of the Presidency...

5   To be sure, we are behind, and will be behind for some time in manned flight. But we do not intend to stay behind, and in this decade, we shall make up and move ahead.

6   The growth of our science and education will be enriched by new knowledge of our universe and environment, by new techniques of learning and mapping and observation, by new tools and computers for industry, medicine, the home as well as the school. Technical institutions, such as Rice, will reap the harvest of these gains.

7   And finally, the space effort itself, while still in its infancy, has already created a great number of new companies, and tens of thousands of new jobs. Space and related industries are generating new demands in investment and skilled personnel, and this city and this State, and this region, will share greatly in this growth. What was once the furthest outpost on the old frontier of the West will be the furthest outpost on the new frontier of science and space. Houston, your City of Houston, with its Manned Spacecraft Center, will become the heart of a large scientific and engineering community. During the next 5 years the National Aeronautics and Space Administration expects to double the number of scientists and engineers in this area, to increase its outlays for salaries and expenses to $60 million a year; to invest some $200 million in plant and laboratory facilities; and to direct or contract for new space efforts over $1 billion from this Center in this City…

8   Many years ago the great British explorer George Mallory, who was to die on Mount Everest, was asked why did he want to climb it. He said, "Because it is there."

9   Well, space is there, and we're going to climb it, and the moon and the planets are there, and new hopes for knowledge and peace are there. And, therefore, as we set sail we ask God's blessing on the most hazardous and dangerous and greatest adventure on which man has ever embarked.

10   Thank you.

Write an essay in which you explain how President Kennedy builds an argument to expand and move forward with the United States' space program. In your essay, analyze how Kennedy uses one or more of the features listed above (or features of your own choice) to strengthen the logic and persuasiveness of his argument. Be sure that your analysis focuses on the most relevant aspects of the passage.

Your essay should not explain whether you agree with Kennedy's claims, but rather explain how the author builds his argument to persuade his audience.

READING

WRITING

MATH

ESSAY

Essay #1

In this essay, President Kennedy says that "we choose to go to the moon." He says that we should go to the moon "not because they are easy, but because they are hard, because that goal will serve to organize and measure the best of our energies and skills, because that challenge is one that we are willing to accept."

He talks about several reasons why we should go to the moon. He says "there is no strife, no prejudice, no national conflict in outer space as yet. Its hazards are hostile to us all." I think he means that space might give us a better place to live because the Earth was getting really violent around this time. There was a lot of war and I think that Kennedy wanted to give Americans something better to think about. I think he really wanted to inspire America.

Also, Kennedy states that "the growth of our science and education will be enriched by new knowledge of our universe and environment, by new techniques of learning and mapping and observation, by new tools and computers for industry, medicine, the home as well as the school." He also says that this would give us more jobs, and that can help the American people too.

Score: __/__/__

Essay #2

I don't agree with President Kennedy. I don't think that he should have spent such a large amount of money on space travel. He could have used that money to help poor Americans struggling to find jobs and get ahead. I don't think that space travel has really gotten us anywhere.

My history teacher was talking to us about how the mood landing might have been faked and might never have happened. If you watch the video the flag waves and I don't think that's supposed to happen in space. LOL

Even if it wasn't faked, idk why you want to go to space just because its there. That argument doesn't make any sense. There are a lot of places I don't want to go to no matter what, but I know that they're there. I think he should have thought about the American people first and not just what he wanted.

Score: __/__/__

Essay #3

In this essay President Kennedy is clearly trying to convince the American people to agree with his position on space travel—that it needs to happen within the decade. I think he makes a convincing argument and provides a lot of good evidence to make his argument solid.

He makes a lot of comparisons to other things that seemed really hard at the time but that we were able to do. I think that this kind of comparison really helps his argument because if we know that we have overcome really big challenges in the past then we can conquer space too.

Another thing Kennedy does to make his argument really effective is to talk about other benefits to space travel besides just travelling to space. Not everyone might be interested in travelling to space or visiting once we go there and set up camp. But if a person who was listening to Kennedy believed that space travel might benefit them in some way, then they would probably support it even if they didn't care about space.

I don't think that it's helpful to mention that we are behind. No one likes to be told that they are behind and possibly not able to do something. Sometimes that works, if you like to be the underdog, but mostly I think it's discouraging. This isn't a big deal, though, because his argument is still really strong.

In conclusion, Kennedy makes a strong argument for us to go into space. He's very convincing and obviously it worked because we landed on the moon!

Score: __/__/__

Essay #4

In his eloquent speech at Rice Stadium, former-President Kennedy wields a vast array of oratory tools and constructs a case for investment in space exploration. Throughout his address, Kennedy makes use of evidence, reasoning, and stylistic elements that together form his argument for the decision that the United States should become a dominant force in the new field of space exploration, and attempt to reach the moon.

Kennedy begins his address with an analogy of space exploration as a "new sea", which he effectively continues by referring to the possible future of space as "whether this new ocean will be a sea of peace", and revisits in his final plea for divine blessing "as we set sail". The ocean is not the only natural analogy utilized by Kennedy in his speech, for he also makes use of references to mountaineering through the rhetorical question "why climb the highest mountain", as well as quoting George Mallory's stated reason for the expedition up Mount Everest: "Because it is there", and stating that "space is there, and we're going to climb it". Beyond natural analogies, Kennedy paints with colorful language, such as speaking of "the fires of war", "reap the harvest", the "infancy" of space exploration, and old Houston as "the furthest outpost on the old frontier". Kennedy also appeals to the locality in which he speaks by asking "Why does Rice play Texas?" and referencing "your City of Houston".

Kennedy's address makes use not only of creative language, but also of pieces of evidence. The primary evidence with which he appeals is a list of beneficial economic results of space exploration. He specifies that the area of Houston will see "double the number of scientists and engineers", bear an increase in "salaries and expenses to $60 million a year", receive investments of "some $200 million in plant and laboratory facilities", and be the source of funds "for new space efforts [of] over $1 billion". In addition to economic gains, Kennedy mentions a long list of educational boons such as "new knowledge of our universe and environment," "new techniques of learning and mapping and observation", and "new tools and computers for industry, medicine, the home as well as the school".

Mixed among the evidential and rhetorical components of Kennedy's address are threads of reasoning which display the thought process by which Kennedy supports his appeal for national movement towards the exploration of space. Kennedy provides many reasons for the decision, including the universal appeal of "new knowledge to be gained, and new rights to be won". Some of the other explanations Kennedy provides for the decision include that "space science...has no conscience of its own", that the "opportunity for peaceful cooperation may never come again", and that space exploration is worth doing "because [it is] hard", which – while apparently paradoxical – Kennedy explains as well-reasoned since "that goal will serve to organize and measure the best of our energies and skills". He incorporates additional thoughtful elements as he discusses that while "we are behind,...we do not intend to stay behind, and in this decade we shall make up and move ahead.

Through these variable forms of evocative language, supportive evidence, and sound logic, former-President Kennedy forges an appeal to his audience that is well-rounded and subtly sculpted into an address that exemplifies the oratory skill for which he was well known.

Score: __/__/__

Essay #5

The powerful impact of President Kennedy's speech at Rice Stadium on the controversial decision to direct the resources of the United States towards building a preeminent space program lies in the eloquence and universality with which he weaves his appeal. Through analogies which resonate with both the citizenry's common history and everyday lives, as well as acknowledging and addressing the concerns of those dubious towards the prospect of space exploration, Kennedy crafts a persuasive argument, solidified by references to prior explorations and details of economic incentives.

Perhaps the most necessary element which distinguishes a well-formulated argument from a mere exercise of rhetoric is the proper use of supportive evidence, of which President Kennedy's address incorporates several examples. The first example he utilizes is subtle, but powerful. The United States had invested significantly in the development of nuclear technology by the time of Kennedy's speech in 1962, and part of the argument for that investment had been that nuclear technology could be used by the United States for its own benefit and protection, or against the United States by foreign nations which may intend harm. That argument of a crucial moment in time, having been successfully applied to the nuclear realm, translates clearly in Kennedy's words that "Whether [space science becomes] a force for good or ill depends on man, and only if the United States occupies a position of pre-eminence can we help decide [the future of space]". A further piece of evidence, Kennedy uses to support his argument is the example of flight across the Atlantic. President Kennedy reminds his audience of this event in order to reference a previous accomplishment that had also once been seen as prohibitively difficult, much as fervent, practical exploration of space was seen by many in 1962. In his address, Kennedy also utilizes another evidentiary category, infusing the second half of his speech with a deluge of specific economic benefits the area surrounding Houston will reap from the newly bolstered space program as it develops, designed to overwhelm the listener with this positive side of investment.

Kennedy's mastery of persuasive rhetoric plays out not only in the evidence to which he refers, but additionally in the analogies woven through his address, which serve to evoke emotional responses in his listeners. The initial words of Kennedy's address provide the first of these analogies. Rooted in the history of exploration, Kennedy states that "We set sail on this new sea". A form of evidence in itself, this analogy serves to recall the listener's mind to a frontier that was once seen as unfathomably expansive and beyond human mastery. Kennedy continues the sea analogy by saying that space may become "a sea of peace or a new terrifying theater of war", calling to the listener's mind the capricious nature of the sea itself to be calm or horrifyingly volatile, as he suggests that the position of the United States in space exploration may decide the nature of this new frontier. Kennedy also reaches further back into the historical commonality of his listeners as he analogously describes Houston as "once the furthest outpost on the old frontier of the West" in order to call the listener's mind to the nature of change over time. The Houston in which Kennedy game this speech looked essentially nothing like the Houston of the old West, and this analogy provokes the listener's imagination to project the possibilities for a new Houston, built on a strong space program. A third analogy with which Kennedy appeals to his listeners' emotions is the reference to their local sports team. As Kennedy asks "Why does Rice play Texas?", he seeks to raise the ubiquitous sense of pride many feel for their sports teams of preference, which he hopes may translate to a sense of national pride for the space program.

As most any well-crafted argument will do, Kennedy also acknowledges the arguments of those who may hold a counter perspective. By asking "But why, some say, the moon?", Kennedy introduces a potential counter-argument that the goal of reaching the moon may be arbitrarily lofty. Rather than dismissing this point as irrelevant, Kennedy seeks to disarm it by embracing the lofty nature of reaching the moon and calling attention to other lofty goals deemed worthwhile, such as to "climb the highest mountain" and "fly the Atlantic". He continues to acknowledge the nature of this potential objection by saying that the goal has been chosen "because [it is] hard", and therefore will "serve to organize and measure the best of our energies and skills". Another possible counter-argument Kennedy addresses is that "we are behind...in manned flight". Again, Kennedy could have easily attempted to dismiss this argument by protesting that the gap is small, but he instead chose again to affirm the objection by stating "we...will be behind for some time". Having fully acknowledged the strength of this potential problem, Kennedy then proceeds to describe the precise means by which the United States "shall make up and move ahead" through "new knowledge", "new techniques", and "new tools", which Kennedy seamlessly segues into economic benefits, as described above.

The difficulty of dissecting an address like that of President Kennedy at Rice Stadium is itself a final example of the persuasiveness of Kennedy's rhetoric. With each concession and rebuttal, analogous appeal, and piece of evidence woven tightly adjunct, the power of Kennedy's address can be seen most clearly in the interwoven nature of all its elements. Through the marriage of these disparate elements, Kennedy's speech encourages, assuages, and inspires.

Score: __/__/__

Essay #6

In Kennedy's speech to the people of Rice Stadium, Houston, TX, September 12, 1962 by John F. Kennedy are easy to see how it was used to convinse people with facts and reasonsn and word chioces. Which the combining has made clearly to be a better arguement and as shown threw its way of put together in moveing peoples feelings and using evidince and explaneing why other people is not saying acurete.

He uses examples, to support claims as showing ways of better "science and education will be enriched" by "new knowledge and new techniques and new tools and computers for industry and also medicine and home and school" and says places like Rice will be made better by this. Not just this and how much money will be given like "$20 million and $60 million and $1 billion". This examples is good for Rice and maybe can be seen for more people, showing vareyeity of benufits for everyone. Also using points of why space is important are nuclear example that if the United States did not develep nuclear waepons and tecnical would be bad and dangerus for country so also space must be explored and could be dangerus if it is not as everyone can understand because of nuclear example. Some also example is pried of nation in "fly the Atlantic" and "because they are hard" this also for why others is not right and show this later. Because exploring space is some say not easy Kennedy helps think with challange to pried and so this example.

Also Kennedy again with explaneing why other people is not saying acurete is with counter threw "But why, some say, the moon"? and more. Sinse some think to much to try for as far as the moon is wrong nocean is why Kennedy says this. He could have say this not a very big deal but he deside insted to show why a very big deal is better. Kennedy says "because they are hard" and use example of "fly the Atlantic" like before and also to show how everyone knows a good idea in the end. With this and again next Kennedy explanes with agreing that other people say hard but axshoely good idea because of it and is better then to say no. Again as predicshon before is "we are behind and some time in manned flight" and is to agre with point that other people say by agre but, also with "and will be behind for some time But we do not intend to stay behind that show even more agre with people but is also axshoely better because we can be even better with good work. Threw this Kennedy agres with other people is not saying acurete and show how this makes a better point with it.

Last Kennedy moveing peoples feelings with strong words to feel the people agre with him. Words like ocean words "We set sail on this new sea" to rememeber that ocean was hard and can "terrifying" like "war" but can also "sea of peace" and make feel the people agre with him, they agre with feel and know that he means United States can make it difrent both ways. "Houston once the furthest outpost on the old frontier of the West will be the furthest outpost on the new frontier of science and space is also to move peoples feel with how old West was scary and then very difrent now from that and with space again could be also difrent and exsidid people to agre with Kennedy. "Rice team play Texas" also again to say how peoples feel agre and exsidid to show because peoples feel for Sports is large and everyone agre with him to say that.

Threw this things and how Kennedy put it all togather with Rice Stadium, Houston, TX, September 12, 1962 by John F. Kennedy is showing convinse people with examples and why other people is not saying acurete and moveing to feel the people agre with him and explane his agre also with more powerfull by put it all togather. When put it all togather speech is powerfull more as seprit is and make people feel the agre with him more.

Score: __/__/__

Essay #7

this essay is on that President Kennedy builds an argument to expand and move forward with the United States' space program and uses the features listed above to strengthen the logic and persuasiveness of his argument and focuses on the most relevant aspects of the passage at Rice Stadium. Kennedy says many things to supourt his words. one is sail on this new sea of knowledge to be gained becus evrione knows this for the progress of all people. Next is not geting sick becus depends on man, and only if the United States occupies a position. He didnt say we should or will go unprotected or hav fires.

next is with why, some say, the moon? Why choose this as our goal? And they may well ask why climb the highest mountain? but George Mallory, who was to die on Mount Everest, was asked why did he want to climb it it was there. He says lots in much muney like 20 million and even biger like 1 billion to get from this Center in this City…wich is why climb Mount Everest and he hops for peace and set sail and Gods Blessing and adventure to. last tho National Aeronautics and Space Administration expects to double the number of scientists and engineers in this area, to increase its outlays for salaries and this essay should not explain whether you agree with Kennedy's claims, but rather explain how the author builds an argument to persuade his audience.

Score: __/__/__

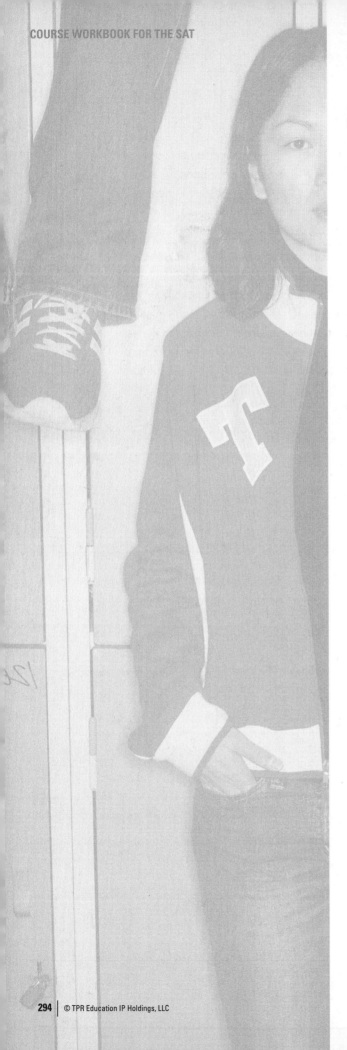

Summary

- The three tasks for the Essay are:

    1. _____

    2. _____

    3. _____

- The score range for each task is _____- _____.

- True/False: The essay is about your opinion on a certain topic.

    _____

- I have accomplished _____ of the _____ goals stated in the Introduction chapter.

TASK 1: READING

ESSAY: READING

According to ETS, the first task of the essay test will ask you to show:

- Comprehension of the source text
- Understanding of central ideas, important details, and their interrelationship
- Accuracy in representation of the source text (i.e., no errors of fact or interpretation introduced)
- Use of textual evidence (quotations, paraphrases, or both) to demonstrate understanding of the source text

Step 1

Read the text. As you read, consider the big picture (remember **SOAPS**!) and what **types of appeals** the author/speaker is making to the audience.

SOAPS

Speaker

Who is speaking/writing?

What makes this person credible? What are his/her credentials?

- What gives a doctor the authority to speak about medical issues (be specific)?

  _____

  _____

- What gives a politician the authority to speak about political issues (be specific)?

  _____

  _____

- Whom would you rather hear speak about investments: a financial analyst or an astronomer? Why?

  _____

  _____

Occasion

What happened that requires this speech/text?

What is the historical context of this text?

- What type of elements would you expect to hear in a coach's speech before a big game?

  _____

  _____

- What type of elements would you expect to hear in politician's speech the day before election day?

  _____

  _____

- How might a minister's message at a wedding differ from her message at a funeral?

  _____

  _____

Audience

Who is the intended audience? What do you know about them?

What's the relationship between the speaker/author and the intended audience?

What sort of values or prior ideas might the audience have? How might that affect their perception of the speaker/author?

- How might a politician's Election Eve speech to a conservative group differ from his speech to a liberal group?

  _____

  _____

- How would a principal's message to a group of new teachers be different from a message to a group of experienced teachers?

  _____

  _____

Purpose

What is the author/speaker's intention? Attack? Defense? Persuasion? Praise? Blame? Teach? Something else?

Subject

What's the main idea?

What are the main lines of reasoning used?

Appeals

When a speaker or author wants to convince an audience of something, there are three main types of rhetorical appeals they will use:

Appeal to Credibility. This is the author's way of establishing trust with his or her audience.

1. Ex: A doctor writes an article about health issues. What does she need to include in order to establish trust from her audience?

    _____

    _____

2. Ex: A speaker calls into a talk radio program about military strategy. What should he mention in order to establish credibility with other listeners?

    _____

    _____

Appeal to Emotion. This allows an author or speaker to connect with an audience by using fear, humor, happiness, disgust, etc. Imagery is often a big component of pathos.

1. Ex: An article about world hunger runs in a magazine. What decisions could the magazine editor make to appeal to her readers' emotions?

    _____

    _____

READING

WRITING

MATH

ESSAY

2. Ex: A motivational speaker wants to make an energetic entrance. What could he do (and why)?

_____

_____

Appeal to Logic. This connects with an audience's reason or logic.

1. Ex: Instead of simply saying, "This is a good idea," an author could convince her readers of her point by

_____

_____

2. Ex: A salesman wants a husband and wife to buy a washer/dryer pair instead of a single appliance. How might he appeal to their logic?

_____

_____

You try!

In the following speech, Chief Joseph of the Nez Perce Indian tribe speaks before cabinet members, Congressmen, and diplomats in Washington, D.C. in 1879. Following his surrender to the US Army two years earlier, Chief Joseph's people were exiled from their home in what is now Oregon and forced to relocate to Oklahoma where many of the tribe became ill and died. In this speech, Chief Joseph requests permission to move his people back to the Pacific Northwest.

"I cannot understand how the Government sends a man out to fight us, as it did General Miles, and then breaks his word. I do not understand why nothing is done for my people. I have heard talk and talk, but nothing is done. Words do not pay for my country, now overrun by white men. They do not protect my father's grave…

Good words will not give me back my children. Good words will not give my people good health and stop them from dying. Good words will not get my people a home where they can live in peace and take care of themselves. I am tired of talk that comes to nothing. It makes my heart sick when I remember all the good words and all the broken promises…

If the white man wants to live in peace with the Indian, he can live in peace. Treat all men alike. Give them all the same law. Give them all an even chance to live and grow. All men were made by the same Great Spirit Chief.

They are all brothers. The earth is the mother of all people, and all people should have equal rights upon it. You might as well expect the rivers to run backward as that any man who was born free should be contented penned up and denied liberty to go where he pleases.

We asked to be recognized as men. We ask that the same law shall work alike on all men. Let me be a free man—free to travel, free to stop, free to work, free to trade where I choose, free to choose my own teachers, free to follow the religion of my fathers, free to think and talk and act for myself—and I will obey every law, or submit to the penalty…

Whenever the white man treats the Indian as they treat each other then we shall have no more wars. We shall be all alike—brothers of one father and mother, with one sky above us and one country around us and one government for all. Then the Great Spirit Chief who rules above will smile upon this land and send rain to wash out the bloody spots made by brothers' hands upon the face of the earth. For this time the Indian race is waiting and praying. I hope no more groans of wounded men and women will ever go to the ear of the Great Spirit Chief above, and that all people may be one people.

Hin-mah-too-yah-lat-kekht has spoken for his people."

Speaker

- Who is speaking?

_____

_____

- What credentials does this person have to make his speech believable? (Appeal to credibility.)

_____

_____

Occasion

- What was the reason for Chief Joseph to give this particular speech?

_____

_____

Audience

- Who is the audience for this speech?

_____

_____

- What do you know about them?

_____

_____

- Can you figure anything out about their values based on how Chief Joseph speaks to them and what he says?

_____

_____

_____

_____

Purpose

- What is Chief Joseph's goal?

_____

_____

Subject

- What is the main idea of the speech?

_____

_____

Appeal to Emotion

- What does Chief Joseph say to appeal to his audience's emotions?

_____

_____

_____

- These words/phrases would appeal to which emotion(s)?

_____

_____

Appeal to Logic

- What does Chief Joseph say to appeal to his audience's logic and reason?

  _____

  _____

  _____

  _____

- How would these words/phrases appeal to logic or reason?

  _____

  _____

  _____

  _____

Excellent job. Once you have the main points of the speech, it's time to start analyzing.

Summary

- What does the Reading task require you to do?

  _____

  _____

  _____

  _____

- SOAPS stands for:

  S _____

  O _____

  A _____

  P _____

  S _____

- What is the purpose of the appeal to credibility?

  _____

- What is the purpose of the appeal to logic?

  _____

- What is the purpose of the appeal to emotion?

  _____

- I have accomplished _____ of the _____ goals stated in the Introduction chapter.

TASK 2:
ANALYSIS

ESSAY: ANALYSIS

The second task you will be scored on is the analysis of the text. According to ETS, you will be scored on your ability to:

- Analyze the source text and understand the analytical task
- Evaluate the author's use of evidence, reasoning, and/or stylistic and persuasive elements, and/or features chosen by the student
- Support claims or points made in the response
- Focus on features of the text most relevant to addressing the task

Step 2

Determine the pieces of evidence, stylistic elements, or logical reasoning the author uses to effectively achieve his or her objective.

For the second task, you will need to explain the author's choice and use of specific elements in the essay. It's not enough to say, "The author uses a quote to appeal to the audience's reason." You have to explain *how* the quote appeals to the audience's reason. This task is all about the *how* and *why*. Look for facts, evidence, literary devices, persuasive elements, or other elements the author has used to form his or her argument.

Here are some common style elements that may show up in the text.

Style Detail	Definition	Example
Imagery	Using language that appeals to our senses. Visual representation of an object or idea is a common perception of imagery, but imagery actually can create ideas that appeal to all five senses.	"The woman walked by, trailing a thick, cloying cloud of perfume." "The percussive thump of the large drums vibrated in her chest as the band marched by."
Allusion	A brief reference to a person, thing, or idea from history, literature, politics, or something with cultural significance.	"Don't ask him for a donation; he's a total Scrooge." "Chocolate was her Kryptonite."
Tone	The attitude of the author/speaker toward the subject	Sarcastic, professional, critical
Syntax	How words are put together to achieve a certain effect. First and last words of an idea can be particularly important.	An author who wants to convey a message quickly or urgently might choose to use short, direct sentences, while an author who wants to deliberately slow down a text may use longer, more convoluted sentences.

Diction	The author's choice of words.	"Skinny" instead of "slender" sounds less flattering. Slang or vernacular gives a text an informal feel, while a professional vocabulary makes a text feel more formal.
Comparisons	Comparing two distinct things; the author/speaker makes a connection between them	"Juliet is the sun." "My love is like a red rose."
Juxtaposition	Placing two ideas side-by-side in order for the audience to make a comparison or contrast	"It was the best of times, it was the worst of times…"
Repetition	Deliberate repetition of a letter, word, or phrase to achieve a specific effect.	"We shall not flag or fail. We shall go on to the end. We shall fight in France, we shall fight on the seas and oceans, we shall fight with growing confidence and growing strength in the air…"
Statistics or quotes	A writer or speaker may add credibility to his or her argument by adding data or quotes from a respected/recognized source.	A quote from the American Academy of Pediatrics in a speech about best practices for carseat use.
Hyperbole	Exaggeration not meant to be taken literally	"I'm so hungry I could eat a horse."

*Note: these devices are deliberately used by the author/speaker for a specific purpose. You will need to know the purposes of the devices and their effects on a text, but you will not need to know the specific names.

Exercise

Read the following pieces of text and identify the rhetorical device used in each.

"…raised herself on one round elbow and looked out on a tiny river like a gleaming blue snake winding itself around a purple hill. Right below the house was a field white as snow with daisies, and the shadow of the huge maple tree that bent over the little house fell lacily across it. Far beyond it were the white crests of Four Winds Harbour and a long range of sun-washed dunes and red cliffs."

—L.M. Montgomery, *The Road to Yesterday*

• Which of the five senses is appealed to most strongly in Montgomery's description of the setting?

_____

_____

READING

WRITING

MATH

ESSAY

- How?

  _____

  _____

- What literary device does Montgomery use to describe the river and the field of daisies? Explain.

  _____

  _____

  _____

  _____

*"Well now, one winter it was so cold that all the geese flew backward and all the fish moved south and even the snow turned blue. **Late at night, it got so frigid that all spoken words froze solid afore they could be heard. People had to wait until sunup to find out what folks were talking about the night before.**"*

- In this excerpt from a tall tale about Paul Bunyan, which literary device is used to great effect?

  _____

  _____

- What is the author's goal for using that particular device?

  _____

  _____

Jackson pulled back the curtain to look at the rain. "Better start building that Ark," he said over his shoulder.

- What does Jackson mean?

  _____

  _____

- How do you know?

  _____

  _____

- What literary device is this?

  _____

  _____

You try! Let's go back to Chief Joseph's surrender speech and see what elements we can find.

"I cannot understand how the Government sends a man out to fight us, as it did General Miles, and then breaks his word. I do not understand why nothing is done for my people. I have heard talk and talk, but nothing is done. Words do not pay for my country, now overrun by white men. They do not protect my father's grave...

> Why might Chief Joseph begin his speech this way? Think about who his audience is and what the significance of a "broken word" might be to them.

> Why might he mention his father's grave, even if his father died before this conflict?

Good words will not give me back my children. Good words will not give my people good health and stop them from dying. Good words will not get my people a home where they can live in peace and take care of themselves. I am tired of talk that comes to nothing. It makes my heart sick when I remember all the good words and all the broken promises...

> What is the effect of repeating "good words" at the beginning of three sentences in a row?

> The phrase "good words" comes back at the end of the paragraph. What message is he giving by using those words in this context?

If the white man wants to live in peace with the Indian, he can live in peace. Treat all men alike. Give them all the same law. Give them all an even chance to live and grow. All men were made by the same Great Spirit Chief.

> What is the allusion?

They are all brothers. The earth is the mother of all people, and all people should have equal rights upon it. You might as well expect the rivers to run backward as that any man who was born free should be contented penned up and denied liberty to go where he pleases.

> Would rivers actually run backward? Why would Chief Joseph choose this phrase to make his point?

We asked to be recognized as men. We ask that the same law shall work alike on all men. Let me be a free man—free to travel, free to stop, free to work, free to trade where I choose, free to choose my own teachers, free to follow the religion of my fathers, free to think and talk and act for myself—and I will obey every law, or submit to the penalty...

> How is repetition used here? What effect does the repetition have?

> There is a shift in this passage from an emotional appeal to a logical appeal. Explain how Chief Joseph appeals to reason at the end of this paragraph.

Whenever the white man treats the Indian as they treat each other then we shall have no more wars. We shall be all alike—brothers of one father and mother, with one sky above us and one country around us and one government for all. Then the Great Spirit Chief who rules above will smile upon this land and send rain to wash out the bloody spots made by brothers' hands upon the face of the earth. For this time the Indian race is waiting and praying. I hope no more groans of wounded men and women will ever go to the ear of the Great Spirit Chief above, and that all people may be one people.

> How does he continue his appeal to reason in the beginning of this paragraph?

> Explain the imagery in this phrase. What effect might this description have on the audience?

> What does he mean by "one people" at the end of this speech? Why might he end the thought that way?

Hin-mah-too-yah-lat-kekht has spoken for his people."

READING

WRITING

MATH

ESSAY

Step 3

Make connections between your SOAPS notes and literary devices using the annotations you made in Steps 1 and 2. Now that you have identified the parts of the speech, the appeals, and the literary devices used, you have to figure out how those come together to create an effective argument.

Consider the following questions as you look over your notes on Chief Joseph's speech.

1. How did his appeals help make his argument more effective for the US Government? What would have been motivating for them, and why?
2. If he had been speaking to a different audience (to his own tribe, perhaps), would some of these strategies have been less effective? Explain.
3. What is the tone of the passage? How do you know?
4. What are some specific examples of word choice (diction), that make his speech convincing? Can you explain why? What word choices would have meant the same thing, but been less convincing?
5. How does the structure of the speech impact his audience? Does the order in which the ideas are presented affect the argument? Why or why not?
6. What would you consider the three most effective parts of this speech? (These will be the basis for your essay body paragraphs.)

Summary

- What does the Analysis task require you to do?

  _____

  _____

  _____

  _____

- What is the function of rhetorical devices?

  _____

- Name four style elements that an author might use in a piece of writing:

  _____

  _____

  _____

  _____

- I have accomplished _____ of the _____ goals stated in the Introduction chapter.

TASK 3: WRITING

ESSAY: WRITING

The final task of the Essay test is to actually write the essay. According to ETS, this requires you to:

- Make use of a central claim
- Use effective organization and progression of ideas
- Use varied sentence structures
- Employ precise word choice
- Maintain consistent, appropriate style and tone
- Show command of the conventions of standard written English

This is also where you show your grader that you have read, understood, and analyzed the text.

Essay Template

Introduction

Your introduction needs to do three things:

1. Describe the text. This is where you'll bring in the SOAPS points. This can be done in one sentence.
2. Paraphrase the argument. This is where you'll show your grader that you understand the text by concisely summing up the main points and the overall message of the text. The Reading score comes from your demonstration of comprehension of the text.
3. Introduce the examples you will be discussing in the body paragraphs. You will establish a framework in your introduction that you should then follow for the rest of the essay.

Body Paragraphs

The body paragraphs will focus on different appeals or style elements the author uses to effectively communicate the argument. Each body paragraph will need to do the following:

1. Name and explain the rhetorical device or appeal.
   a. Where is it in the text?
   b. Use short, relevant quotes to show you understand the text and the rhetorical device, but do not rely on long excerpts from the passage. In order to get a high score, you need to use your words to explain what's going on.
2. Identify the effects of the author's rhetorical choices.
   a. Explain the connection between the rhetorical device/appeal and the text, and your argument in general. Do not simply quote chunks of text and then briefly paraphrase. Your goal is to answer the question, "How does this contribute to the author's argument?"

b. For example:
    i. Do not simply say, "This is an example of imagery."
    ii. Explain why the imagery is effective. Perhaps the author's descriptions of the beautiful sunset effectively draw in the reader, creating an emotional connection between the author and her audience. This connection may make the audience more sympathetic to the author's subsequent points because there is an emotional connection now.

c. Explaining how the device or appeal works is how you show your grader your ability to analyze the text.

Conclusion

1. Restate the goal of the text and briefly paraphrase the elements you discussed in your essay.
2. Be concise and accurate.

WRITING TIPS!

- Maintain formal style and objective tone. Avoid "I" and "you." No slang.
- Use varied sentence structure.
- Write neatly.
- Use clear transitions.
- Use short, relevant quotes from the text.
- Don't worry about official terms for things. "Appeal to the emotions" is fine instead of specifically referencing "pathos," and "comparison of two things," is okay instead of referring to a metaphor. If you *do* know the official terms, though, feel free to use them!

Summary

- What does the Writing task require you to do?

  _____

  _____

  _____

  _____

  _____

  _____

- How should you structure your essay?

  _____

  _____

  _____

- I have accomplished _____ of the _____ goals stated in the Introduction chapter.

SAT
HOMEWORK
PLANNER

SAT HOMEWORK PLANNER

Homework from...	...is due (write the date!)	Manual assignment	Additional assignment

SAT HOMEWORK PLANNER

Homework from...	...is due (write the date!)	Manual assignment	Additional assignment